THE RUODLIEB

THE RUODLIEB

THE FIRST MEDIEVAL EPIC OF CHIVALRY FROM ELEVENTH-CENTURY GERMANY

TRANSLATED FROM THE LATIN
WITH AN INTRODUCTION

BY

GORDON B. FORD JR.
Northwestern University

LEIDEN
E. J. BRILL
1965

PRINTED IN THE NETHERLANDS

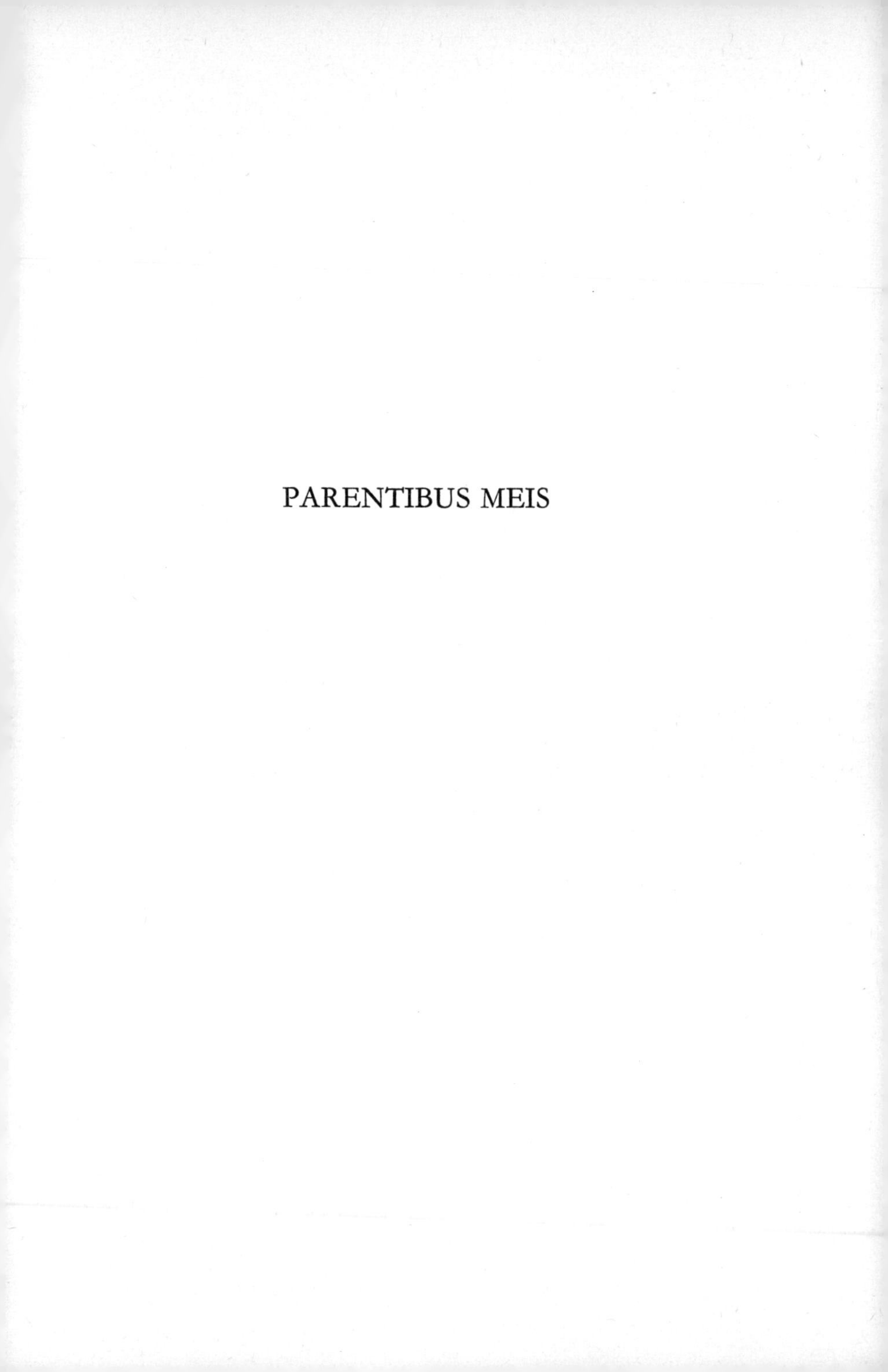

PARENTIBUS MEIS

CONTENTS

INTRODUCTION

The *Ruodlieb* is a Medieval Latin epic poem about the adventures of a German knight named Ruodlieb at the court of an African king, in a rural environment, at the castle of a widowed chatelaine and her daughter, at home with his family, and with a dwarf.

The name of the author of the *Ruodlieb* is unknown. Since seventeen of the eighteen double leaves of the original manuscript were separated from the binding of later manuscripts which originated at Tegernsee, the monastic center of Bavaria, it is likely that the *Ruodlieb* was written by a monk at Tegernsee. Until the end of the nineteenth century most German scholars attributed the work to Froumund, a poet who flourished at Tegernsee in the early part of the eleventh century, but this view is no longer held because of the vast differences in the styles of the two authors. There is no doubt, however, that the author of the *Ruodlieb* was German. This is evident from the German proper names (Ruodlieb, Immunch, Hartunch, Heriburg), the German fish names in Fragment X, the rhyming German words of the love greeting or *Liebesgruss* in Fragment XVII, and some German idioms in Latin form.

Because of the supposed references in the poem to the

Mainz jewelry of Empress Gisela, the mother of Emperor Henry III (1017–1056), a known patron of the arts, to the meeting of the two kings in Fragment V, which may have been inspired by a real historical event, such as the meeting of Emperor Henry II of Germany with King Robert II of France in 1023, and to the Byzantine gold pieces described in Fragment V, with the figure of Christ standing beside the emperor and placing His hand on him in blessing, the poem has traditionally been dated about the middle of the eleventh century. However, the palaeographer Anton Chroust, *Monumenta Palaeographica*, Ser. II, Vol. I, Part 2, Plate 7 (Munich, 1911) says that the hand of the original manuscript, now in the Bavarian State Library in Munich, appears to belong to the time of Abbot Sigfrid (1048–1069) or to the beginning of that of Abbot Eberhard (1069–1091). Since the internal evidence mentioned above is by no means so reliable as the palaeographical for dating the poem, I prefer Chroust's later date of about 1060–1070 A.D.

We do not even know what the poet entitled his work. The name *Ruodlieb* was given to it by its first editor, Andreas Schmeller, after the principal character in the poem, who, strangely enough, is not mentioned by name until Fragment V and not again until Fragment XII. The poet, it seems, had a particular fondness for omitting the names of his characters. He must have looked upon them as representative types and not as specific individuals. He designated his hero as an exile, hunter, commander-in-chief, envoy, and knight, and other characters as merely the king, the redhead, the huntsman, the chatelaine, the cousin, the young lady, and the mother.

The text of the *Ruodlieb*, which consists of eighteen fragments and about 2300 extant verses, was discovered at the beginning of the nineteenth century by B. J. Docen, who was the librarian of the Bavarian State Library in Munich. He noticed the *Ruodlieb* on some irregularly cut strips of parchment in the bindings of a few manuscripts which had come from Tegernsee. Docen began copying the fragments which he had found, and his successor, Andreas Schmeller, who discovered additional fragments in Munich, continued the work begun by Docen. In 1840 two more leaves of the same manuscript were found in Dachau. The eighteen double parchment leaves discovered in Munich and Dachau constitute the Munich manuscript, Clm. 19486, which dates from after the middle of the eleventh century. These eighteen double leaves are generally believed to be parts of an autograph, and because of the numerous erasures and corrections in the text, it is quite likely that they belong to the first draft of the unknown poet. Besides the Munich manuscript there exists a fragment of another manuscript containing all of Fragment XI and part of Fragment XIII, which was found in 1830 at the St. Florian Monastery near Linz, Austria. Of its 140 verses only 23 agree with the original, and thus it contains 117 entirely new verses. The St. Florian manuscript is of later date than the Munich manuscript, from which it was probably copied, but also belongs to the eleventh century. Both manuscripts were cut so as to be used in binding other works and consequently have been seriously mutilated. In some passages, therefore, part of the first half of a verse is lacking, and in other passages part of the last half is missing. Because of the gaps in the text and the uncertainty of some of the restorations which have been proposed, the difficulties which a translator of the *Ruodlieb* faces are great. In my translation I have included summaries of action which occurred in parts which have not survived. How much of the poem is lost is not known, but the complete work probably contained no more than 3500 lines and perhaps as few as 2800 lines.

It may be questioned whether we have the end of the poem. The subject matter of the last fragment, where Ruodlieb subdues a dwarf and is promised his help in winning a kingdom, the treasure of two kings, Immunch and Hartunch, and Immunch's daughter Heriburg in marriage, is different from that of the other fragments because it does not pertain to the real world, upon which the poet has previously focused his attention, but to the legendary world of Germanic heroic saga. The text breaks off abruptly before the end of the last manuscript page after the dwarf's wife has pleaded with Ruodlieb to hold her as a hostage until her husband has done what he promised. On the back of this same page there are only seven epigrams having no connection with the text. It is likely, therefore, that the poet intentionally ended his work at this point and desired to leave Ruodlieb's future crowning and marriage to the reader's imagination. It seems that the legendary world was of less interest to him than the real world. Indeed, his love for realism, exemplified in his descriptions of animals, plants, clothing, jewelry, art objects, and, most of all, of human types from the merciful great king to the evil redhead, characterizes the entire poem.

In addition to the text of the *Ruodlieb*, there are also preserved eleven epigrams of two to eight hexameters each, which were written on the reverse sides of the first and last parchment pages of the Munich manuscript. They describe such things as bellows, wine casks, and greaves. One praises four ancient inventors of musical instruments.

The meter which the poet employed is the dactylic hexameter with leonine rhyme. By this is meant that the last syllable of each verse rhymes with the first syllable of the third foot of the verse.

The *Ruodlieb* belongs to an age of transition and has a varied subject matter derived from different sources. For this reason, it has been variously called an heroic epic, an epic romance, a courtly novel, and a didactic poem. The *Ruodlieb* actually belongs in a special category by itself and it is difficult to decide what this category should be called. The great king, who plays a leading role in the first half of the poem, is the very embodiment of all the Christian virtues, as is Ruodlieb himself, whose service at the great king's court gives him an opportunity to associate with a king whose Christian qualities he will imitate as a Christian knight and later when he becomes a Christian king himself. The *Ruodlieb* heralds a new era of courtly knighthood based upon an ideal of Christian humanitarianism and thus may be considered the first medieval epic of chivalry.

The first edition of the *Ruodlieb* was done by Jakob Grimm and Andreas Schmeller in 1838 and appeared in their *Lateinische Gedichte des 10. und 11. Jahrhunderts* (Göttingen, 1838), although the text of the St. Florian fragment had already been published in Moriz Haupt's *Exempla poesis medii aevi* (Vienna, 1834). The Dachau fragments, which Grimm and Schmeller's edition did not include because they had not yet been discovered at the time of its publication in 1838, were later published in *Haupt's Zeitschrift* I, pp. 401–404. The only complete edition of the *Ruodlieb* did not appear until 1882 when Friedrich Seiler in his *Ruodlieb, der älteste Roman des Mittelalters nebst Epigrammen* (Halle, 1882) edited the entire poem with a lengthy introduction, copious textual notes, many emendations, and a valuable glossary. Seiler's edition, however, was almost immediately supplemented by an extensive review by Ludwig Laistner, which appeared in the *Anzeiger für deutsches Altertum* IX (1883), pp. 70–104 and by an important article by Laistner in which he showed on internal evidence that Seiler's arrangement of the fragments (I, II, III, IV, V, VI, VII, VIII, XI, XII, XIII, IX, X, XV, XIV, XVI, XVII, XVIII) was wrong. This appeared in the *Zeitschrift für deutsches Altertum* XXIX (1885), pp. 1–25. Karl Langosch in his *Waltharius, Ruodlieb, Märchenepen: Lateinische*

Epik des Mittelalters mit deutschen Versen (Basel, 1956) printed Seiler's text, taking into account the two supplementary articles by Laistner and the latter's new arrangement of the fragments as well as articles written by Strecker and several other scholars. Langosch was primarily interested in translating the poem into German verse and thus did not make any original textual contributions. Langosch's text was used as the basis for the present English translation. In my translation of the *Ruodlieb*, however, I have also incorporated suggestions and conjectures made in my own three articles: "Some Textual Notes on the Fifth Fragment of the *Ruodlieb*" in the *Zeitschrift für deutsches Altertum* XCIII (1964), pp. 291–292, "*Ruodlieb* VI, 85–87; 90–92" in *Latomus* XXIV (1965), and "*Ruodlieb* V. 196: The Problem of the Meaning of *Glans*" in *Classica et Mediaevalia* XXV (1965). In 1959 appeared the edition of Edwin H. Zeydel, *Ruodlieb: The Earliest Courtly Novel (After 1050)*, (Chapel Hill, North Carolina, 1959). Zeydel also accepted Laistner's rearrangement of the fragments and added several conjectural supplements. On the whole, however, his text does not differ much from that printed by Langosch except for his additional conjectural supplements. A new textual edition of the *Ruodlieb* with photocopies of both manuscripts of the poem, a linguistic introduction, and an enlarged glossary with citations is now being prepared by the present translator.

There have been three previous German translations of the *Ruodlieb*, all in verse: Moriz Heyne, *Rudlieb* (Leipzig,

1897); Paul von Winterfeld, *Deutsche Dichter des lateinischen Mittelalters in deutschen Versen* (Munich, 1913); and Karl Langosch, *Waltharius, Ruodlieb, Märchenepen: Lateinische Epik des Mittelalters mit deutschen Versen* (Basel, 1956). All of these translations deviate too much from the original and cannot be relied upon for accuracy. The only previous English translation of the *Ruodlieb* was made by Edwin H. Zeydel in his *Ruodlieb: The Earliest Courtly Novel (After 1050)*, (Chapel Hill, 1959). Zeydel's translation is quite literal, so much so that tenses fluctuate from present to past in the same sentence, and contains some inaccuracies.

An excellent article in English stressing the importance of the *Ruodlieb* is one by Helena M. Gamer, "The Ruodlieb and Tradition," *ARV: Tidskrift för Nordisk Folkminnes-forskning* XI (1955), pp. 65–103, which contains a thorough discussion of the literary sources and cultural value of the poem. Professor Gamer rightly emphasizes that the "contents (of the *Ruodlieb*) are the unique and precious literary testimony for important aspects of mediaeval life in Germany during the eleventh century" (p. 65) and that the poem is of interest to specialists in many different fields, such as medieval history, literary history, legal history, linguistics, and folklore.

Werner Braun's *Studien zum Ruodlieb: Ritterideal, Erzählstruktur und Darstellungsstil* (Berlin, 1962), which is concerned with the knightly ideal, the structure of the narrative, and the style of presentation of the poem, is also a very valuable contribution to studies on the *Ruodlieb*.

FRAGMENT I

RUODLIEB'S DEPARTURE FROM HIS HOMELAND

A certain hero (Ruodlieb), born of a noble family, adorned his inherited nobility with his character. He is said to have had many wealthy lords. Although he served them often according to their wishes, he was unable to obtain any of the honors which he thought that he deserved. He did not put off whatever any of these lords entrusted to him—whether it was to avenge them or to transact their business—but accomplished it as energetically as possible. Often he risked his life for these same lords in war and in hunting and in every type of action. They gave him nothing because faithless fortune prohibited. They continued to promise, but always ignored their promises. Since he could not overcome the enmities which he had incurred on their account, he was at a loss to know what to do about it.

Realizing that he could live nowhere securely, he arranged all his things and entrusted them to his mother and at last departed from his country to seek foreign kingdoms. No one accompanied him except his squire, who carried his pack loaded with various things and whom he had taught from boyhood to endure labor for him. The squire carried the pack on his right shoulder and his master's shield over the left. He bore a lance in his right hand and a quiver under the shield. A very adequate small sack of food was in his possession. His master was clad in mail and covered with a coat besides. For headdress he wore a gleaming steel helmet. He was girt with a sword adorned with gold as far as the hilt. From his snow-white neck hung the claw of a griffin—not a whole claw, but one only half a cubit long. In back where it was wide and in front where it was narrow, it was decorated with pure gold and a deer-skin strap. It was not white like snow but translucent like a jewel, and when he blew it, it resounded better than a horn. At last he said goodbye to his mother and to the whole household. His horse stood black as a raven and, as if washed with soap, was completely speckled with white everywhere amid this blackness. Its mane, embracing its neck, lay on the left side. The horse had been ornamented with trappings in a way befitting every noble. Nothing was seen to be tied to his saddle except a vessel sewed from leather—and besmeared with aromatic resin so that the drink poured into it would taste sweeter—and a small pillow made of purple cloth. When he jumped on the horse, the horse itself jumped higher, as if rejoicing that its master had mounted bravely. The knight's dog, which could run very swiftly, jumped sometimes in front of him and sometimes behind him. It was a hunting dog, and there was none better. In its presence a beast, whether large or small, could not conceal itself without the dog's finding it quickly. At last, telling his mother and his servants goodbye, his face moistened with tears, he kissed everybody. Seizing the reins and goading his horse with his spur, he dashed over the plain as swiftly as a swallow flies. In the enclosed area his mother feasted her eyes upon him, and all the servants, mounting on a fence, looked after him, sobbed, wept, and sighed. When they could no longer see him, their lamentation increased. After all of them had wiped off their tears and washed their faces, they went quickly to console their mistress. Feigning hope, she suppressed her sorrow deep in her heart and consoled them when she saw that they were suffering.

In the meantime, certainly no less care oppressed her son, and on his way he reflected about very many things: how he had not been able to gain any advantage at home and how, on account of the many feuds in which he had become involved, he had had to go into exile from his sweet fatherland. He thought to himself that if he served a lord as vassal for little pay anywhere and if his old fortune were further ill-disposed toward him, all his associates there would be inimical to him, and he would not better his situation but would find it worse. Sighing deeply and weeping, he asked the Lord most earnestly not to desert him or to allow him to die, but to come to his aid so that he might overcome his hardships.

RUODLIEB MEETS A FOREIGN KING'S HUNTSMAN

When the knight in his sorrowful state entered the

foreign kingdom, the king's huntsman suddenly became his companion. The huntsman greeted the knight and was greeted by him in return. The exile (Ruodlieb) was strong in limbs and masculine in countenance, eloquent in speech, and serious in response. The native asked him who he was, where he came from, and where he wished to go. Ruodlieb did not reply but kept disdainfully silent. The hunter was sorry that he had inquired how his situation was and reflected: "If he is an envoy, his retinue is too small. If he is coming to court, who is carrying his gifts and his sword? I think he is of poor means but of abundant virtue." When he had been silent for a long time, at length he said to Ruodlieb again: "Do not become angry if I ask you more questions! For I desire to help you if I can, not to hurt you. I am the king's huntsman and am dear and loyal to him. He is accustomed to listen to no one more graciously than he listens to me. If you have left your fatherland because of violent feuding and if in this country, which is as foreign to me as it is to you, you wish to earn a living and to overcome your misfortunes, then I shall give you some useful advice, which should not be refused. Provided you have learned well the art of hunting, how favorable are the auspices under which you have come into exile here! The king loves this art and anyone skilled in it. Whoever has something is able to give; tell me, what can he who has nothing give? If not daily, nevertheless, the king will give you gifts quite often. You will never have worries about food or clothing. When beautiful swift horses are given to the king, they are first entrusted to us so that they may be tested in running to see which is fast and easy to ride and not rebellious. The king gives the horse to that man who needs it the most. You will never spend one penny on fodder for that will be given to you without measure whenever you desire it. Passing over the wealthy counts at the table, he talks and jokes with us instead when he dines. He passes to us whatever good food is served him and does this more for our honor than for our remuneration. If you would like to enter into a bond of loyalty with me, let us pledge our good faith and join our right hands in alliance so that nothing may separate us except bitter death. Wherever we may be, let each of us so plead the causes of the other as if they were his own, if he can possibly plead them better." Then the exile, at last trusting the hunter, said to him: "Sir, you have thoroughly demonstrated your kindly will toward me, and I do not think that your advice should be ignored, for indeed you have correctly guessed what my situation is. Hence I desire that a compact of loyalty be established between us." They gave their right hands to each other there and immediately became comrades. They kissed each other and were established as firm friends, serving each other with one heart.

RUODLIEB'S SERVICE AT THE COURT OF THE GREAT KING

When they had thoroughly disposed of the matters between them, they began to approach the capital of the kingdom where the king imposed his law on the people arriving. They entered the castle, where they stabled their horses and settled their squires, and hurried together to the court to see the king. When the king saw the hunter, he said to him: "Tell us where you have come from and what news you bring. When you went through the forest, did you track down a bear or a boar which we should like to pursue?" The hunter responded not as to a master but as to a friend: "I have tracked down neither of them but have discovered one who can subdue them and have brought him with me to you—I am referring to this youth, who is fit to serve you, very skilled in the art of hunting, and very blessed, as I think and as appeared to me in his company. When you deign, you can test him thoroughly yourself. He is bringing his gifts to you, which are small but not to be rejected, and desires that you take him into your vassalage." Ruodlieb held with his left hand his two-colored dog to whose neck was fastened a golden chain.

FRAGMENT II

(Ruodlieb was graciously received by the king and demonstrated to him his skill in fishing with an herb called bugloss.)

Medical men say that the power of that herb (bugloss) is such that if it is roasted, ground, and mixed with a little flour and if pellets are made from it in the shape of beans and are tossed into the water, any fish that eats one of them cannot swim beneath the water but only on its surface.

The pellets, which he had made round by turning them in three fingers, were scattered into the lake, where fish in a large school swarmed eagerly, each taking a pellet for itself. Those which tasted them could no longer swim under water but, making high leaps as if in play, dispersed in every direction and could not submerge. Ruodlieb and his oarsman moved across the lake in a boat and drove the fish to dry land with a stick. The two men surrounded them with a net under the surface so that when they came to land, the fish would not be able to leap back into the water. Ruodlieb and his companion made a sport of fishing in such a way. Then they ordered the cooks to bake the small fish over glowing coals but carried the large ones on a shield to the king and joked: "This is the best we could do today!"

The king asked: "Did you catch them with nets or hooks or seines?" The native huntsman replied: "We don't fish that way but induce the fish to come to us from the depths against their will and to provide us with great sport by leaping over the water. When they cannot go back under water and are very tired from leaping, at last, by means of a stick, we make them come to rest on land." "This I wish to observe," the king said, "when there is an opportunity."

Pliny, writing about the powers of various herbs, praises bugloss as very suitable for many purposes. Whoever puts it into a strong drink, he states, cannot get drunk, no matter how much he drinks. Pliny also states that if someone should sprinkle some of the same powder over meat and happen to give it to a dog, the dog would be blinded by it in a short time. Also, according to Pliny, any animal which was temporarily blind at birth would very quickly lose its sight if it tasted any of the powder. The huntsman, an ardent lover of this herb, went into a forest where he knew there were many wolves; with him was his companion, who led a she-goat by a rope. The two slew it there under the broad shadow of a beech tree, removed the skin, and cut the flesh into pieces, which they sprinkled with the powder and concealed in the skin. Then both climbed up a tree and sat waiting. The exile (Ruodlieb), emitting the horrible howls of wolves, sometimes uttered the loud sounds of old wolves and sometimes the soft ones of their young, so that you would have thought real wolves were howling. When the wolves assembled there, they found the she-goat, which they tore to pieces and devoured in a moment. They did not go far from there before they lost the sight of both eyes.

WAR BREAKS OUT

The foreign knight devoted himself eagerly to such things and the like and furnished himself to all as zealously as he could while the kingdom enjoyed great peace and honor. The border neighbors of the other realm were very friendly to us, and this friendship was maintained by our people themselves. They went to each other's countries to purchase whatever they wanted, sometimes paying the toll and sometimes collecting it. Our girls married their men, and they gave us their daughters in marriage. They became mutual godparents, and those who were not were called so. This friendship lasted between both peoples for many years until the bonds of peace were broken by crimes. The despiser of our peace and our common enemy did not cease to sow the seed of discord so that wherever there was good faith, it would not remain there perpetually. Since he succeeded, a large war suddenly broke out and many persons were killed for little reason at a certain market place where many had gathered.

FRAGMENT III

(After the count of the neighboring kingdom invaded and attacked Ruodlieb's adopted land, the king appointed Ruodlieb commander-in-chief of his forces, which defeated the count's troops and took him prisoner. When the count insisted that not he himself but his king was responsible for the attack, Ruodlieb contradicted him with these words:)

"I know that your king is so wise that he did not order this but that instead your foolish pride urged it. Now you shall see what kind of honor you will obtain for this. You aggravated the situation when you desired to make a name for yourself. You thoroughly deserve to be hanged from a branch by the calves of your legs."

Everyone shouted and asked why he was slow in doing this. The commander answered: "Our king did not order us to destroy anyone who either surrendered or was captured but, if we could, to rescue the prisoners together with the booty. Both of these things we have done properly. Who wishes greater honor than to vanquish a victor? Be a lion in battle but like a lamb when taking vengeance! It is not honorable to you to avenge grievous losses. The best kind of vengeance is when you spare your wrath. Therefore, so that it may be done with your approval, please agree that the count may go with us alone and unarmed, either on his own or on just any horse as you prefer, unless you want one squire to serve him in order to take his horse, stable it, and feed it. Grant also that he may see not only his own people walking before him in chains but also into what shame and danger he has led them so that he will not rashly presume to commit such a crime again." Then all told him that his words were agreeable to them and with great jubilation quickly returned to their own country.Although they saw that their houses were burning, they were not depressed because they enjoyed liberty.

The commander, the chiefs, and the other vassals of the king went to the border town and there secured their prisoners. They counted their comrades, rejoiced heartily that all were well, and gave praise to God. A messenger was sent to the king to report everything and to bring back word about what he wanted them to do with the pillagers. The messenger asked for his horse to be brought to him in a hurry. When the squire brought it, he gave the messenger at the same time a stick from the hedge. The messenger mounted his horse and by striking it compelled it to fly. With his spur he caused the horse's side to be stained with blood. The watchman of the king, beholding him from a high rock, shouted: "I see a young man who is making great haste to bring news; he appears to be excited for no little cause." Many, eager for news, met him, caught hold of his horse, and asked him what he had to report. Telling them "hello"—no more, no less—he gave his sword to his squire and hurried to the king himself. The knight said:

"You who are the everlasting royal pillar of your people and are very worthy of praise, live happily, hail, rejoice!" The king replied to the knight: "Please tell me, are our vassals safe? Who were slain in battle? Inform me whether the booty taken from us has been recovered." The messenger, who was surrounded on all sides by a large crowd, bowed and replied: "Your Majesty, do not think any such thought! Rejoice, for no one of your vassals has perished, and now all the booty is returned entire, without damage. Now my comrades have inquired and asked through me what they should do about the captives whom they have reduced to chains. I have been commissioned, Your Majesty, to tell you nothing except this." The king ordered that three gold marks be given to the envoy, who was exceedingly gladdened by the gift, and said: "My friend, return quickly and tell your comrades this from me: 'The king sends thanks to you in word and deed. Come to him with your prisoners as quickly as possible!'" Bowing, the youth hastened to his horse in order to return. The trip, which had taken two hours before, now took only one. Very good pay is always responsible for hurrying things up. When the messenger returned, he ordered all his comrades to assemble. They came together and stood in a wide court. Then the envoy said to them throughout the enclosed area: "The king bade me express immense thanks to you not only in words but in deeds which will follow the words. He wants you to come to him as quickly as possible and commands you not to release any of the plunderers."

FRAGMENT IV

THE PEACE NEGOTIATIONS

(Ruodlieb and his victorious army returned home with the count and the other prisoners, The great king treated them mercifully, especially the count, who was given special privileges. Then the great king sent Ruodlieb to the court of the lesser king to offer him forgiveness and to arrange peace negotiations. Ruodlieb was well received by the lesser king, who discussed his reply to the great king with his advisers in the following speech:)

"Now there is need for us to decide how we should thank the great king for his mercy in more than words alone, of which we shall find enough. We must also determine what various gifts we should send him as, for example, horses elegantly decorated with reins of gold, gray skin coats, and colorful fur cloaks. Each of you must tell me what he wishes to contribute for this purpose."

They replied together that they would do this very willingly. The king thanked them and then said to them: "Tell me first what I should reply to the messengers." There was one philosopher there wiser than all, whom neither fear nor love was able to divert at all from the right when he made a decision. They said that he should speak for them and implored him to do so. The philosopher, saying that the king's will would be best, advised that the king's counsel alone should be followed. The king said: "Since you are allowing me to make the decision, it remains that the envoys come here and speak their words so that you may know from them whether or not you wish to believe them."

He sent for them. When they came, he said to them: "Look, I have announced the pleasant message full of good faith from your king, who is your lord and our friend: how mercifully he has treated those whom he could deservedly destroy and whom, although worthy of death, he is returning to me safe and sound against his own interest. He has mercifully offered us much honor. My people and I both should earn this mercy if he will do what he promised through you." The envoy said: "He is not so disposed that he is accustomed to go back on his word. What he says is true, for he desires that his word be true." The king said: "You say when and where the meeting will take place." The envoy replied: "It is your right to stipulate this, Your Majesty." The king said: "You, nevertheless, name the place where we should assemble so that peace may be secured between us for a thousand years." The messenger replied: "If you wish and if it pleases these lords of yours, I know no place so well suited for your meeting as that field on which we previously fought, between the boundaries of our kingdoms, so that where your people were conquered and ours were freed, yours may be reconciled with us and released." That place seemed to all to be very suitable for this purpose and spacious enough for both kings to meet. They agreed upon the peace negotiations for three weeks thence. After this the king rose, dismissed his council, and retired with a few to his chamber to rest.

Very good royal gifts were given to the envoys, who returned to the king and gave due thanks to him. He ordered that some of the best wine which he had be poured for them. The envoys rose and asked that they be given leave. The king said: "Listen to me, my friends, and pay attention to what I say to you. Tell these things to your king not as to a friend but as to a father returning good for evil: 'Your legation which came to us disclosed that you are such in your heart as you reveal yourself in your words, and by promising pardon to the guilty and by giving hope of safety, exhibited thoroughly your wonderful intention of voluntary clemency, in return for which we cannot give you adequate thanks. But, having been subdued in battle, we are subject to you and will always be heartily ready for every kind of service. As you have offered in your message, we are ready to go wherever you wish. It has seemed best to your people as well as to our own that the meeting, which has been agreed upon for three weeks hence, should take place on the battlefield where you first suggested.' If I have forgotten anything, your good faith will complete it." They responded together: "You sufficiently deserve that we serve you always with a loyal heart." Then they bowed and departed with a proper farewell.

Next they went, as was proper, to the vicegerent, by whom they were richly provided with gifts and blessed with his farewell. In accordance with the order of the king, the vicegerent gave them a guide to see that they would have what they needed. He accomplished this with the utmost zeal and with a loyal heart until he had led them peacefully and honorably beyond the border delimiting the territory of the kingdom. They asked their guide, after he had been amply presented with gifts and thanked with words, to bow to his king, and he replied, "I shall do so." They separated from him and returned to their own country.

When they returned home, they quickly went to see their own king. As soon as he saw them, he received them cordially and said: "Tell me what news you bring me now." The messenger answered: "Because Christ is kindly toward you, merciful God voluntarily grants to you without effort on your part that which other kings do not achieve except with great force. For throughout the kingdoms which are adjacent to you on all sides, you are believed to be a lion with an eye always vigilant. Indeed, with your lamblike clemency and your wisdom you conquer better than the sword of another could conquer. For with God as my witness, in the place to which you recently sent me, I did not know whether you were more loved or feared by them. When the lesser king had heard (the group of his nobles was also present) what you offered him and all his people together—first, service and then the love of a loyal heart—he removed his crown, rose, and bowed honorably. Then, sitting down, he kept silent until he had heard the matter fully: how his countrymen and ours had quarreled; how his forces, attacking ours unexpectedly, had slain, despoiled, and burned the captives; how our soldiers had subdued the enemy, freed the captives, and bound the captors; when our men had brought the enemy's soldiers to you and the latter thought they would perish, how mercifully you had taken pity on them by relieving them of their fear, absolving them, consoling them, and treating them well; how you had given them to the bishops and the wealthy dukes so that they might serve them and feed their horses; how our soldiers had not treated them with imprisonment or with force of fetter as they deserved, but in a way that befitted friends of the king, so that when they would be returned they would not happen to complain of their treatment. In fact, I told the lesser king how you had committed to no one the very count who had perpetrated this enormous crime and that you completely trusted no one to be in charge of him, but that he served you and carried his sword very often, so that no one would harm a man whom the king thus honored. After I told the lesser king that you were unwilling to remember the immense shame and the unspeakable loss inflicted upon you by those who are now under your jurisdiction, I said further that if he wished, you would promise to return them unpunished, although they deserved punishment as enemies, and injured in no respect, so that peace might be restored between the people on both sides. Having thus spoken, I became silent and sat down at the king's direction. He postponed giving a reply to these things until the next day.

"Early on the following morning all went to the court, more desirous of news than of the king's honor. Those who seemed to be at all useful were admitted so that they might give advice to their king on such a matter. The doors were closed, and what they said is not known. There was a brief conference to get the opinion of the counselors. Meanwhile, a very sumptuous lunch was served to us. While we were still eating and drinking wine, someone was sent after the three of us to tell us all to come. We did as he ordered. When we came before the king, he said: 'Messengers of our lord and of our highest protector, if we knew how to reply well and honorably to your merciful and fatherly message, we should do so promptly as your king very much deserves. Now tell him from me and from all my people, from the great, the average, and the lowly, who are legally subject to me, of the loyal and ready service of my subjects. Your wonderful virtue and your great clemency and wisdom so adorn you everywhere externally as they fill you within. We know that we are unequal to you in wealth and in knights and that if you wished, you could destroy us as we deserve. To return evil with good is very great vengeance. For one is feared all the more when he does that by which he is known. Your great power and incomparable will are like a wall for you, which no one can overthrow. It is unheard of that the one injured pray for pardon for him who injured and that he take pity on him! Do you not rightly seem to us to act like God when you are indulgent to sinners of your own accord without their asking? In return, we are able to offer nothing similar, but we should implore with our heart and with our lips that the King whom you are thus imitating will later reward you. That you will live for a long time, be well, rule, and be rich is to be desired earnestly and entreated in common by us and by all the neighboring kingdoms on all sides. For you alone are our pillar in the place of Christ. As long as you are alive we can rule well under the shield of your good faith, safe for a very long time. Now, my lord, do not disdain to come to the places agreed upon since they have been stipulated. We shall come to you from our people and serve you.' Thus he spoke. He enriched us with very splendid gifts—skin coats, decorated horses, and fur cloaks. Then he asked for wine, which was drunk with Saint Gertrude's toast and shared with us three. Finally, kissing us, he sighed after us and blessed us when he said farewell. We went away from him and went to see the vicegerent who, presenting us with gifts and providing us with a guide at the same time, kissed us according to custom and dismissed us with great love, offering to you, as his lord, his devoted service. Thus very friendly leave was given to us by all. Our guide served us with propriety and with honor and with singleness of purpose until we saw the boundaries of this large kingdom."

The king, rejoicing in such news and such honor, smiled

a little and uttered no proud word from his lips. Looking up, he praised the Lord through whose will he had gained the victory. Attributing nothing to himself but giving God all the credit, he said: "Tell me where and when the peace negotiations have been arranged." "When three weeks have passed, the peace negotiations will take place on that field where we contended before, freed our men, and reduced the enemy to chains, in order that the enemy may be gladdened on the spot where they were saddened. Thus I stipulated and promised to the king on your behalf." The great king said: "I approve this promise and I shall not break it. Tell me, what did you have to do while you were there?" The knight replied: "The vicegerent was gracious to me and provided me with much so that I would not suffer any want. Frequently he tried to beat me in a game of chess but could not unless one game were given to him intentionally. For five days he did not allow me to come before the king, for he wished to discover what my arrival there meant. After he could not learn this by any device, the king sent for me and listened intently to what I said to him. His answer was deferred to the next day, as I have already said. The king, asking for a chess board, ordered that a chair be brought for him and bade me sit down on a stool opposite him so that I might play with him. This I persistently refused, saying, 'It is terrible for an inferior man to play with a king.' But when I saw that I dare not oppose him, I agreed to play, desiring to be beaten by him. I said: 'What does it matter that I, an inferior man, be defeated by a king? But I am afraid, my lord, that you will soon become angry at me if luck aids me so that the victory falls to me.' The king said with a smile as if he were joking: 'There is no need, my friend, to fear anything about this situation. If I never win, I shall not become excited. But I want you to play with me as seriously as you know how, for I desire to learn the moves which you will make that I don't know.' Immediately both the king and I moved eagerly and, may thanks be to her, Victory fell to me three times. Many of his nobles were quite surprised at this. The king bet with me but did not allow me to bet him anything, and he paid what he bet until not one pea remained. Many followed, who wished to avenge him. Furnishing security but refusing mine, they were certain that they would lose nothing and trusted completely to doubtful luck. They helped each other but by receiving help only hurt themselves more. Since they were advised variously, they were hindered, so that amid their dispute I quickly won. This happened three times, for I did not wish to play longer. They desired to pay me immediately what they had bet. At first I refused, for I thought it wrong that I be thus enriched and that they be impoverished by me. I said: 'I am not accustomed to make any profit when I play.' They replied: 'As long as you are among us, live as we do. When you return home, you can live there as you like.' After I had resisted them persistently, I accepted what they offered. Thus Fortune gave me profit and praise." The great king said: "I think that you should always love this game, by which you have become so well heeled. Now accept my thanks for pleading our cause well."

The great king sent instructions to all those who held prisoners to clothe them honorably and bring them to him. He directed that those who were footsoldiers should return as cavalrymen, armed as if they were ready for new wars. He clothed the count like one of his own chieftains with two expensive skin coats and as many fur cloaks. He gave him a scarlet coat sparkling with jewels and gold, in which he was to serve cups of wine to his own king. The great king also gave the count a strong, swift, and very steady-gaited horse having a gilded bridle and beautiful trappings. He gave him a suit of armor, in which he could be safe in every general war and duel. He also provided him with a sword, a helmet, and a sharp lance. To both the vassals who served him were given very good garments, which were always rare in their country. Moreover, he furnished them with weapons appropriate for war. The king dispatched heralds to call his vassals and counts to come to his court as well-dressed as they could and to bring with them whatever they and their horses would need for staying three weeks or longer with him. Wise pontiffs and devout abbots, well qualified to counsel, were also invited there.

FRAGMENT V

THE MEETING OF THE TWO KINGS

(The great king arrived at the battlefield where the war had previously been fought with his retinue and all the prisoners.)

The wide court of the great king was enclosed by railings. It was empty in the middle but was surrounded by lodges all around on the outside. In this court the king had enough room to eat lunch and dinner with his twelve bishops and twelve abbots. Adjacent to the enclosed court stood a very large tent facing the east, from which they had put a walkway. At its end they had set up a tent, in which there was a table covered as an altar, and on it were placed the cross and the crown of the king. There they were accustomed to hold the service of Mass for the king, both matins and vespers, with other daily services interposed according to custom. After the great king came there, he heard the Mass immediately and sent a message to the lesser king through the same envoy who had previously been the intermediary in these matters to see him before lunch. When he saw the messenger, the lesser king received him with a friendly smile and kissed him. Then he said to the messenger: "What news do you bring? You thoroughly deserve that I give you my best wishes." The envoy replied: "My king has sent me to you and has ordered me to tell you that you should not have lunch until you have seen him. He is coming to meet you at the bridge which separates us from you. Peace will be made there, and every matter will be recorded. The prisoners will be returned and will not complain that they have been captives, for they will return enriched, not reduced to poverty." The lesser king said, "So be it." The messenger returned to his lord.

When the kings assembled where they had agreed upon, they said absolutely nothing to each other until they had kissed. Our king ordered all the pontiffs to do the same and then kissed all the abbots in succession. Then the same friendliness was accorded to his bishops. When the kings, pontiffs, abbots, and all the clergy had sat down together after the dukes and nobles of both sides had been received, the great king said wisely: "O king, most beloved by all of us, as I agreed and promised to you in my message, let us forget whatever stupidity our people on both sides have committed and let us reconcile them so that they may be concordant with each other without deceit. Let no one recall what adversity he suffered; let him forget revenge and not think about it. For I prefer to return good for evil rather than to overcome evil with evil." The other king rose to thank our king fittingly. Forbidden by our king, he sat down, yet spoke as follows: "For so many and so great kindnesses bestowed upon us we are not able to return to you adequate thanks. He, under whose protection you bore victorious arms, offers you much glory and every honor. Hence there is no need to praise or to commend you. Your virtue and clemency and your liberal generosity would heap rewards of glory upon you, even if all were unwilling. I myself and my people have an obligation to serve you because we were conquered in war and subjected to your standard." The great king said: "This shall never happen, nor shall it ever come to pass so long as I live that any of your right or honor be lessened. You are a king just as I am. I do not wish to place myself above you. You have the same right and the same honor that I do. Let us now accomplish that very thing for which we have come here. Take back your people with every honor." Thus speaking, the great king returned the count shining with regal garments and armed as if ready to wage war. Thus of those nine hundred he returned none without their being armed and suitably clothed. Afterward he said: "These, my king, are the ones whom fate allowed to live and who, when they prevailed over us, treated us not humanely but maliciously with conflagration, plundering, and slaughter. But, on the other hand, when they have returned home, order them to tell you how I treated them in opposite fashion. Now let them come to terms and be as they were before, firm friends and faithful comrades hereafter." After this was done, peace was indeed established on both sides by an oath positively not to be broken by either side.

Then both kings returned to their tents and had lunch with their own vassals. There was great joy in the camp of the lesser king. Everyone rejoiced because his friend had returned safely. After the table had been removed, each one set aside very many gifts, which were to be given to the great king and to those who accompanied him. Five hundred talents of gold were to be given to the king, in addition to much silver and a hundred cloaks, a hundred byrnies, and as many steel helmets. Along with the horses there were thirty decorated mules, thirty wild asses, just as many camels, two leopards, two lions, and an equal number of twin bears. The bears were black on their legs and paws but otherwise completely white as snow. They picked up vessels and walked on two legs like human beings. When mimes touched the strings of their instruments with their fingers and played, the bears danced and kept time with their paws. Sometimes they leaped and turned somersaults. They carried each other on their backs, sat down, embraced each other, wrestled, and threw each other down. When the people did a loud-sounding dance and circled around, the bears ran up and joined the women, who sang pleasantly with a weak voice. After they placed their paws in the ladies' beautiful hands, the bears stamped in an upright position step by step and growled, so that those who were stepping around there were amazed and were not angered for whatever harm they suffered. Moreover, the lesser king added to the gifts a lynx, an animal produced from a fox and a wolf. This was a gift not without value, for from its urine is formed a clear jewel, the glittering ligure, which is as precious as a carbuncle. Let him who pleases learn how it is made!

Have four nails made for you from iron. Fix them into four places in a wide tub and drive them in so strongly that no one can pull them out. In the middle of the tub make an opening with a drill. Place the wild animal into it, even if it should be unwilling and rebellious. Take care to bind its paws well to the nails and around its neck hang a fastened chain. Bend its head so that it may not be able to break its bonds. Give it enough to eat and to drink, but what it drinks should be a potent wine, sweet to drink. After it is drunk, the lynx will not be able to hold the wine even if it wishes to. Let its urine pass without its knowledge, as if it were retained, and flow quickly into a basin through the bored tub. If the lynx cannot pass its urine, it will die. And yet if the animal should not void the urine and should retain it even in death, draw away its skin, carefully open its abdomen, remove the bladder and puncture it minutely with a needle. Then press the urine into a very clean basin and pour it into small copper vessels the size of a pea or into vessels the size of a large nut. Bury these vessels in the ground and let them remain there for fifteen days. Then dig them up and recover them. You will see that all the drops have been formed into jewels, which shine in the blackness of night like glowing coals. Some should be set in the rings of queens, but mount and fit the large ones into the crown of a king.

Although they had no value, an ape with a short nose, a naked hind end, and a truncated tail, and a long-tailed monkey with the voice of a hawk and with gray skin were added to the gifts. In both of these creatures no usefulness is seen. From the family of birds the lesser king added royal gifts of two parrots, two ravens, jackdaws, and starlings, which were well versed in chattering with words. They were eager to imitate whatever they heard. The lesser king honorably provided gifts for each pontiff. He presented the dukes with byrnies, helmets, and shields and also with horns decorated in front and in back with gold. He gave the counts beautiful cloaks of marten fur and gray horses, and the high knights skin coats and fur cloaks.

After this had been so disposed of, the lesser king wished to rest a short while. He ordered that it be found out when the other king would arise. Later, after he awoke, he got up and ordered that his mule be saddled. Then with those whom he wished he rode to the great king. Many ran to meet him and were eager to serve him. The great king received him cordially and asked him to sit down. The lesser king said: "My lord, deign to come with me and do not refuse the small gifts which I shall present to you. I ask that all your highest lords here come with you also." The great king replied: "So be it." The other king returned home. The great king summoned his highest lords to assemble. After they had come together and had sat down in his presence, their king, as was always his custom, ordered them to value their honor more than the lesser king's gifts and not to accept whatever the lesser king wished to give them: "Do not let it appear that you need his wealth. Come now with me and do what I do."

They went with their king and were honorably received. After they had sat down and had prepared and drunk three toasts, the lesser king led the great king and those whom the latter had ordered to go with him to a wide court enclosed by railings. There stood tables heaped with various treasure; there stood horses decorated in a manner as becomes a king; there stood mules and enormous camels; there stood thirty wild asses, which were gentle and tame; there stood frightful leopards and lions. You too, lynx, stood there, fastened on a golden chain. The ape with the long-tailed monkey stood tied up there. There stood two bears with much variety of play. There were even birds there, which enjoyed the speech of human beings: the parrot, the raven, the jackdaw, the magpie, and the starling. Then the lesser king said: "My good king, all these gifts shall be yours. These shall be for the bishops and those for their vassals." The lesser king desired to give thirty pounds of gold to each one. Fifty pounds of silver were to be given to the clerks of the royal chapel and as many to the household servants. Among the squires and the low household servants twenty pounds of coins were to be distributed. The lesser king did not pass over the waiters without giving gifts to them also; he gave to each of the twelve the same amount, namely ten pounds, to be divided among them. Then he presented the dukes with helmets, byrnies, swords, golden shields, and melodious trumpets for battle. Sixty pounds were to be given to their servants. Then the lesser king bestowed upon the counts horses equipped with trappings and ten pounds to be given to all their servants. Finally he offered his prayers to all the twelve abbots and promised them his service. He gave to each of them and to the brethren who followed them thirty pounds, and to each of their servants one pound. He sent to the monastery fifteen pounds for the monks. To the great king's confidential advisers and to the other vassals who were in his daily service and were always bombarding the king's ears and helping anyone for a high price, he gave exceptional gifts valued at a thousand talents. Among them he provided the foreign hunter (Ruodlieb) with abundant gifts and treated his colleague in the same way, both of whom had been envoys to him and had executed the peace.

After the great king had seen these gifts and had examined them carefully, he said to the lesser king: "Your gifts are very fine. Yet lest you be burdened by us as a result of so much giving, we have decided to accept your vow instead of your gifts. I shall take those two bears which played so comically, and for my daughter I shall accept from you the magpie and the starling. You shall have as many thanks as if you had given me everything. I do not want you to give anything to the bishops, the dukes, or the counts. What you give to the monks and abbots, I shall not object to, for that will truly be repaid to you. They are constant in serving the Almighty and pray for you zealously night and day. What you give them will occasion bright joys for you. I do not want you to give more gifts to the highest lords." Whether the great king was silent about the household servants intentionally or forgetfully, they were well provided for secretly and made happy. The lesser king did not dare to give anyone a large or small gift contrary to this edict, nor did any of the great king's vassals desire it.

RUODLIEB RECEIVES A LETTER FROM HIS MOTHER

After the kings said farewell to each other and kissed each other, they desired to return to their respective countries. When they returned home and came under their own jurisdiction, Ruodlieb, seeing unexpectedly a certain messenger who had come to him from his beloved mother, received him cordially. He said this to the messenger: "Tell me whether my mother is well." The messenger answered: "She is alive and very well and sent this little letter to you, which you may believe more than you believe me." Ruodlieb took the letter and had a scholar read it. When he had read it over, the scholar said: "I think this letter says: 'All of us, your lords, who are very kindly disposed toward you, ask that you return. For we grieve to have been without you for such a long time. It was on account of us that you went into exile and did not cease to heap feuds upon yourself until, fleeing from your homeland, you went to foreign kingdoms, where we know that you have endured many hardships. This fact we lament, whenever and wherever we assemble at a meeting of a court of justice and at set proceedings. Then in giving advice no one is equal to you.

There is no one who passes judgment either so justly or so honorably as you and who so protects widows and orphans, who lament exceedingly whenever they are condemned on account of unjust avarice and are oppressed. Now since all your enemies have been eliminated—some are dead, and others have mutilated limbs—so that none of them will harm you again, return quickly, dear friend, because we long for you to come, especially so that we may be completely reconciled with you and give you the presents which you very often deserved for not sparing your own life on our behalf.' But at the end of this letter is a message from your mother: 'My dear son, remember your poor mother, whom, as you know, you left unconsoled and twice widowed, once by your father and for the second time by you, my son, when you departed. As long as you were with me, you alleviated all my troubles. When you departed, you increased my sighing. Yet I decided to bear it somehow, provided you were able to spend your wretched life safe from your so many, so strong, and so dire enemies. Because they are all maimed or slain, return, my dear son, and put an end to your mother's sorrow! By your arrival make not only your relatives happy but all your fellow countrymen as well!'"

After he heard all this, the knight was very much gladdened, but his face was moistened with tears on account of his lonely mother. When his companion found this out through the report of the people, his heart became very sad beyond belief. Not only he but all the squires as well grieved deeply when they were standing or sitting together. They said that they had never seen a man equal to him in honesty of character or in integrity of good faith and that he never harmed anyone but helped everybody whenever he could. Those who knew of his daily service said: "It is no wonder if it is now burdensome for him to have gained nothing for his service except a meager existence, his food, and his clothing with no further remuneration, even though he is the special pillar of this entire kingdom."

Taking his beloved companion with him, Ruodlieb stepped up to the king, before whom he spoke and entreated as follows: "My king, if I dared and if I knew that it would not be painful for you, I should like to inform you what distresses me very much." The king said: "Speak! You have my gracious attention for this." Ruodlieb embraced the feet of the king and kissed them. Then he got up again and could scarcely utter these words for his sighs: "The king himself had better see what my situation is." Thus he spoke and put into the king's hands the letter which had been sent to him. After the letter was read, the king said: "Now I sympathize with your situation very much. If your lords will thus pay you what they promise you, I advise you to go to see them and not to neglect going at once. The message of your mother is also very pleasant. For this reason I do not wish at all to dissuade you now from going to her and consoling her and your relatives, who are very desirous of seeing you. Go whenever you wish, yet remain with us for the period of this week. Do not go before we deliberate about what reward we should give you. You have served us as devotedly as you knew how. We should not forget this but remember it and reward you for so often risking your life for me and for our people, in short for our whole nation." Then the exile bowed and rejoiced that the king remembered his service. He answered the king in few words: "How well you have rewarded me for serving you! After I came here, gracious king, and subjected myself to you, every day with you has always been Easter to me. I have always had many honors and good things not only from you but from every one of your people."

Meanwhile the king ordered that silver vessels be made in the shape of large dishes, a cubit in circumference—not more than four, two of them flat and an equal number of them deep. When they were fitted together, they would look as if they were loaves of bread, provided they had been sprinkled on the outside with flour made of spelt. Of these vessels the king filled one with coins, which goldsmiths call bezants, so close together that he could not force in one more with a hammer. He did this so that they would not happen to move and make a noise. When Ruodlieb returned home, he would better his situation with these coins and make his lords kindly disposed toward him by his generosity so that they would give him the promised presents with a gracious mind. The other dish was divided into two sections and was filled up in this way: in one part of the dish the king placed coins made of gold and thoroughly tested in fire, to which people gave their name from the city of

Byzantium. On one side of the coins was engraved the image of Christ with a Greek inscription around the edge, and on the other side appeared the power of the king. Christ was standing and placing His hand on the king whom He designated as blessed. Ruodlieb was to give the coins to beloved relatives and friends, as was the custom, for the purpose of rejoicing that he was safe and had not been reduced to poverty in harsh exile but had been successful and had returned home with honor. The king placed twelve decorated bracelets on the other side of the section of the dish so stuffed with coins. Eight of them were solid, neither hollow nor filled with lead. They were provided with heads in the shape of serpents, which kissed each other but did not harm themselves in their love. Each of them bore the heavy weight of pure gold. The remaining four were bent in a circle, and each one was round like a hepatic vein and weighed a mark. The king desired that they be useful as well as beautiful. Moreover, there was added to these gifts a large brooch suitable for a queen, which had been cast in clay and had neither been made with hammers nor constructed with any craftsman's tool. It was completely solid and not at all trimmed. In the middle of the brooch was the image of a flying eagle, and in the tip of its beak was a crystal ball, in which three little birds seemed to move as if they were alive and ready to fly about. A golden ring surrounded this eagle in a circle. The brooch was so wide that it covered the breast of the wearer completely. It was wide for good reason since it had been cast from a talent of gold. The king added other brooches lighter in weight, and on each of them the splendor of many kinds of jewels was varied, as if you beheld a group of stars there. Each of these brooches weighed a fourth of a full pound and hung on a chain, which was not large but fine. He added to these a small clasp, which one could put in front and with which one could fasten his shirt every day so that it would not stand open, lest the chest be seen if it were somewhat large. Moreover, the king added a solid lune of gold, weighing one pound, on which a craftsman had brought forth his skill. On the outside and inside curves were set precious stones of all colors, which had been obtained in the month of May from sea shells which had been mixed with golden dew and then shut according to custom. There were fine globules of various types on the surface. Glass is attracted by glass, but is repelled by gold, forming knots, leaves, and little birds. At first they become rough in the flames and, full of humps, are then polished on a rough stone with saliva or water. This honorable substance is called enamel. But behind the jewels on the gleaming rim of the lune, little ornaments gave a pleasant noise by colliding with each other. The king ordered that this lune be added to the dish carefully. He then placed eight earrings into the dish. Four of them sparkled and were adorned with various precious stones, amethysts, and beryls. The four others, however, were not encircled with jewels but were lovely windings varied with wonderful knots as if with a paintbrush one should paint glass with gold. The little ornaments and pearls jingled when the ear moved. Finally the king ordered that thirty rings be made of the best pure gold. On each of these rings he ordered that a ligure, a jacinth, and a beautiful beryl be enclosed and set. Three of them were to be given to the bride whom Ruodlieb would marry. They were not large but were fine as was becoming for women to wear. After the dishes were filled with these royal gifts and were firmly joined together with nails that had heads, the king ordered that they be covered over with a very strong glue. Flour milled with much grinding had been mixed with the glue so that it could not be scratched away nor destroyed by water.

When the day came on which the king had stipulated that he would respond graciously to his vassal, he said to his nobles: "Our foreign knight, recalled by a letter from his lords, wishes to return home. It is on their account, as you know, that he is absent from his own country. Look, here is the letter. Now listen to what it says!" Thus he spoke, and a scholar read it aloud. When he had finished reading the letter, their hearts became sad because the king and they themselves were soon to lose a comrade who was so loyal, so gentle, and so kindly and was such an outstanding young warrior. They urged the king to keep him by force or by entreaty, to give him a wife, and to enrich him with honors, saying that he was worthy of any count's office. The king said: "It shall not happen that he be oppressed by me. By him I have never been moved to the least anger, but rather he makes me as gentle as a lamb when I am angry and shows himself full of complete loyalty in everything. For the burden of his long exile is so grievous to him that I have never been able to observe its like in anyone else. Now let us dismiss him and allow him to return to his homeland. He shall have these thanks: if later his situation is such that he cannot remain at home, he can well return here and find his old advantages with us." Thus the king spoke and ordered a page to call Ruodlieb to him. He ran and called him. Ruodlieb came to the king. After he had been silent for a little while, the king said to him kindly: "My dear friend, only very unwillingly shall I let you go from me. You were always ready and complied in everything. Hence, my very dear friend, I give you great thanks. No one dislikes you, but you are dear to all my people. Now tell me the truth, dearest of all men, whether you prefer that I give you your reward in money or in wisdom." Ruodlieb thought over in his mind what he should fittingly respond to him: "I do not desire," he said, "what common custom renders equal to honor. Wealth, when it is known, attracts many plotters. Poverty compels many poor men to be thieves. It brings enmity to relatives and friends and arouses a brother to break the bonds of loyalty. It is better that one lack wealth than all his sense. Whoever tries to flourish with devout wisdom will always have much silver and gold. He accomplishes what he wishes because he abounds with inner weapons. But I remember that I have very frequently seen many foolish persons who were living in need and degenerating shamefully because all their wealth had been lost through stupidity. It was apparent that wealth had not helped them but had actually done them harm. Therefore, you can easily teach me a lesson which will be as valuable as if someone should give me ten pounds, provided I preserve it and do not violate it. No one will take it away from me or be hostile to me or hate me because of it, nor will any robber kill me in a narrow place on its account. Rich treasure should be only in the chamber of a king. A poor man has enough if he is strong and skillful. I do not desire money; I thirst only to taste wisdom." After the king heard this, he got up and said, "Come with me!" They walked into his inner chamber and allowed no one to come along with them.

THE GREAT KING'S TWELVE PRECEPTS OF WISDOM

The king, sitting down while his vassal, the exile, then stood before him, said in particular: "Now listen from the depths of your heart to what I shall advise you as a true friend to a friend!

1) Never let a redheaded man be a special friend of yours! If he becomes angry, he will not be mindful of loyalty, for violent, dreadful, and enduring is his wrath. He will not be so good that there will be no deceit in him, by which you cannot help being defiled. For if you touch pitch, you can scarcely be cleansed to the nail.

2) Although the much trodden road through the village is muddy, never avoid the road and go through sown fields

lest you be treated badly and be deprived of your reins there after being rebuked by someone and giving a proud answer.

3) Where you see that an old man has a young wife, do not request that lodgings be given you when you are travelling, for you will put great suspicion on yourself even if you are innocent. The husband will be afraid, and his wife will be hopeful: the wheel of fortune so turns between them. But request lodgings where a young man is married to an old widow. He will not be afraid, and she will not love you. Then you will sleep there securely without suspicion.

4) If a fellow citizen asks that he be provided with a pregnant mare which is at the time of bearing, so that he can harrow his little piece of land, do not lend her unless you wish her to be ruined; for she will lose her foal if she has to level the little field.

5) Let no relative of yours be so dear to you that you are accustomed to burden him often with visits. That which is rare is wont to be more pleasing than that which is customary. For whatever becomes frequent quickly becomes contemptible to a man.

6) Do not treat your maid, even if she is very beautiful, as your social equal like a wife lest she despise you and answer you proudly or lest she think that she ought to be mistress over the house if she spends the night with you and sits at your table. Eating with you and sleeping with you all night long, she will immediately wish to be the supreme mistress of everything. Such things make a reputable man ignominious.

7) If you desire to marry a noble wife for the sake of producing dear children, then seek a woman of high repute for yourself and look nowhere except where your mother advises you! When you have found her, you should honor her in every way and treat her kindly. Nevertheless, be her master lest she dare to have any quarrel with you. For no disgrace can be greater for men than if they have been subjected to those whom they ought to rule. Although she agree completely with you in everything, you should never disclose to her your every intention, so that if she later wishes to reprove you after being rebuked by you for a wrong act, she may not be able to say anything to you which would lessen the respect and love between you in any way.

8) Let no sudden wrath seize you so severely that you do not spare your vengeance for the night, especially when the situation is doubtful and is not as was reported to you. Perhaps you will rejoice the next day that you held the reins of your temper.

9) Never let there be strife between you and your lord or master. For masters will overcome you with force if not by law. Do not lend anything to them because you will certainly lose it. When one asks you to lend something to him, in that case it is better for you to give it to him because he will find a fault by means of which he will take the same thing from you. Both will be lost, for he will return neither thanks nor your property. When you have been robbed by him, he will say, "Thank you." Then bow and praise the

Lord that you are getting away safely with your life and consider your losses of no consequence!

10) Never let your trip anywhere be so hurried that you pass by where you see churches without committing yourself to their saints and praying. Wherever a bell is rung or Mass is sung, dismount from your horse and run there in a hurry so that you may be able to participate in the Catholic peace. This will not lengthen your trip but in fact will shorten it very much. You will go from there more securely and will fear your enemy less.

11) Never refuse if any man urges you and begs you to break the fast on account of love for merciful Christ, for you will not break it but will fulfill His commandments.

12) If your fields are near the public roads, do not make ditches lest further advances be made onto your fields. For a road surrounding the ditches is made on both sides when people walk on the dry ground. If you do not dig them, you will have less damage."

RUODLIEB'S DEPARTURE FROM THE COURT OF THE GREAT KING

When the king became silent and ended his words of wisdom, both he and Ruodlieb came forth. The king sat down on his throne and praised to all the virtue of his knight. In turn, the murmuring of those praising Ruodlieb increased. The knight returned thanks to the king and to all his people. The king said: "Go home, full of every honor, and see both your mother and all your possessions, yet only if you can live in your fatherland as in this country and if your lords are willing to do what they have promised. If they deceive you, you should deceive them in return and should not serve them since you have been deluded by them so often! Serve no one who is either very stingy or dishonorable! If it should happen that your mind vacillates and you are disgusted with your own country, if you return to me, you will find me of the same disposition toward you as I am now when I dismiss you. Have no doubt of this!" Then the king motioned with his finger to the page standing before him and, according to his custom, whispered secretly into his ear that the chamberlain should bring him those knapsacks within which were the rich loaves sprinkled with flour on the outside and full of money inside. After the knapsacks were brought, the king said: "My dearest good friend, never break these two loaves until you come to your mother, who is so dear to you. In her sight alone break the smaller loaf. Break the second one only when you enter into marriage with your bride. As much of this as you wish should be given to your beloved friends so that they may taste how our bread is accustomed to be." The king, saying farewell, kissed Ruodlieb three times and dismissed him with a sigh. The knight departed in tears. All the people mournfully followed him to his horse. And when they had said farewell, they wept and kissed him. Then he departed with only his friend accompanying him. The squire, who had carried there only a small knapsack, now led a beast of burden loaded with various riches. A great complaint was made by the beloved comrades that they would enjoy each other for only a short time more. They rode together and talked for not less than three days. They put off eating their supper until midnight. After dinner both took off their shoes. After they decided to go to bed to sleep, turning away from each other, they wept silently and sighed tearfully. Like a boy, Ruodlieb's friend wept more and was quite moved because he had to be separated from a friend so loyal to him. He did not know whether he would ever see Ruodlieb again in this world. He would have wished to spend a sleepless night, wide-awake and crying, if sleep had not quickly fallen upon his grieving heart. When it became day, both woke up at the same time, arose, dressed, had breakfast, saddled their horses, and then proceeded together until they saw the borders of the other kingdom, where at last they were to be separated. The exile, as well as he could for weeping, barely said to his friend: "Dear friend, please tell my lord from my true and virtuous heart of my prayer and devoted service and tell this also to all his people, whom I shall always love with all my heart." While they kissed each other, both cried very deeply. Farewell was said again and again by both. In such a way they sadly departed from each other for their own countries.

THE ADVENTURE WITH THE REDHEAD

As soon as the knight began to approach his own country, a redheaded man saw him and ran up and joined him. After the redhead greeted Ruodlieb, he asked him where he was coming from, where he wished to go, and whether he would be his companion. The knight answered him very disdainfully but wisely: "This is a public road. You can go wherever you wish." The redhead began to utter many words, although he did not receive any response from the knight. Since, as day wore on, Ruodlieb was unable to wear his cape, he tied it to the saddle behind him as he was accustomed. The redhead pondered deeply how he might acquire it. They proceeded, came to water, and there let their horses drink. By stroking the back of Ruodlieb's horse as if he were wiping it off, the redhead secretly snatched the strap and from it the cape for himself. He held it under his armpit until he departed from the water. Then, leaping from his horse, he hastened to stuff it into his sack when he lingered behind the knight as if to determine whether each hoof of his horse's feet had its nails. Then he ran up to the knight and said to him fawningly: "My good man, didn't you appear to me before to have a cape on your saddle? I am surprised that I do not see it." The knight said to him: "I wonder where it may be." The redheaded man said: "Something or other flowed away in the water. Thus perhaps we lost it where our horses drank. Therefore, let us return to see whether we can find it." "No!" the knight said, pretending it were of no consequence to him.

Then in the evening they began to approach a village, through which a very wide and muddy road ran. No one on horseback could get out of the pools nor could anyone on foot have proceeded on such a muddy road next to the fence unless there had been a very narrow bridge. If one tried this bridge and held the fence with his hand, he would scarcely avoid falling into the mud. But there was a narrow path trodden from the road through the fields which gave a way. The redhead was urging that they use this path, saying that he could not ride in a flood of mud and that he knew no road so muddy or so full of water.

FRAGMENT VI

(After the owners of the land where the redhead had trespassed in avoiding the muddy road had censured him, he complained about his treatment to Ruodlieb, who declared that he had been justly treated.)

"Afterwards when you commit a crime, do not curse him whom you are harming because a double injury is very grievous to bear if one loses his property and endures a curse besides." In return, the redhead made very empty threats, saying that the night would not pass before they were maimed, because he wished to inflame all. The knight smiled, for he knew that the redhead would fare worse.

They approached the village where they wished to spend the night. The sun sank into the ocean, and this was a warning for them to seek lodgings. The redhead called a shepherd to come toward him. He came, and the redhead immediately asked him: "Tell me the names of your distinguished neighbors. Is there any rich person here who could be our host?" The shepherd replied: "There are many here, who, I know for sure, would not be amazed if a count with a hundred military units should come to them and who could serve them with every honor. He would be a poor man who could not adequately serve you and stable your horses. Although many are accustomed to serve guests, no one among them all receives the people who arrive as well as do a young man and his old wife." The redhead asked: "Why is the young man married to an old widow? An old man ought to have an old wife." The shepherd replied: "Nowhere could he have found a better wife than she is. He was very poor before he married her. Now he is lord over the woman whom he once served as a servant and is worthy of it because he is devout and kindly. May thanks be to God, who thus took pity on a poor man." Then the knight said: "Please tell me, my friend, how it happened that a rich woman married a poor man." Then the shepherd replied: "Sir, tell me whether or not you have heard that an old ewe lamb eagerly licks a vessel for love of salt. The man to whom she was married before was most dreadful to live with, for he was disagreeable, stingy, and very rarely happy. People never saw him laughing or joking. He could scarcely say how many cattle or bees or horses he had. He did not know the number he had of each. Rarely, however, were the couple filled with the meat of their own cattle. Instead they ate hard cheeses and drank whey. They sold whatever they had and hid the money carefully. The pleasant young man, coming here bare and needy, went to the husband and at first begged bread from him. The old man gave him scarcely one small mouthful of rye. When the youth received it, he stood respectfully and ate it. After the table was removed, he hurried to put away the vessels lest the cat urinate on them or the dog defile them, washed them zealously, and then put them back into the cabinet. He took care to save a spoon for his master at the table so that he might place it before him when he had lunch or dinner. A knife along with salt and the spoon were put on the table. If anything was not well seasoned, whether it was cabbage or broth or any other food, he would season it with the salt. The old man noticed this in his heart even if he did not say anything. The youth omitted nothing that he saw was necessary: he gave water to the cows as well as to the sheep, pigs, and goats; he brought hay to the horses whom he fed. He did these things of his own accord at no one's request. If there was need of anything else, he accomplished it eagerly. After he had been at the old man's house for three days, the latter gave him nothing to eat except a small bite of bread. When he could no longer endure his hunger and desired to set out to another place, he bowed to the old man, who said to him when he saw him leaving: 'Now remain here only two or three more days until we have observed the habits of each other.' The young man agreed, and at once his supply of bread was increased. A fourth of a pound was given to him in the morning, and in the evening he received another fourth. Meanwhile the old man asked him whether he had learned any skill. 'Tell me what better skill I could learn than how to make many sumptuous dishes from cheap ingredients, from herbs and flour. In addition to these I ask for nothing except milk, a little grease, and enough salt to give a pleasant taste. There is another thing, Sir, which is absolutely necessary for us. If I tell you, you must not become angry.' 'Tell me what it is,' he said. 'I shall not become angry.' The youth said: 'Look at yourself: you seem to all to be very rich, but your bread lacks every pleasantness because it is full of bran, dark, and bitter with darnel. If you are willing to give me a peck and a half of any kind of flour so that I can make bread, I shall present to you bread well sifted, seasoned with parsley seed, and besprinkled with salt; and some cakes smeared over with lard; and ring-shaped buns and other bread in the shape of the penis. In doing this, I shall not diminish the quantity of your bread. Whatever I sift out, I shall store very carefully in a vessel and give to your chickens and to your noisy geese. If I shall break bread for distribution among your servants, I shall not give them so much that you may seem lenient to them. In doing this, I shall put the whole household at your service. Be present to inspect everything, leaning on your cane.' The old man, seeing that the youth was very wise, entrusted to him the care of all his property so that he might look out for his possessions and his servants, as he desired. The youth did this with such caution and such care that nothing was wanting to his master or to any of his household. He took nothing for himself beyond the allowance allotted him and often struggled to clothe himself. He served his master in this way with the utmost loyalty and without deceit for I don't know how long. Then that scoundrel died. There was no one who ever lived, who was meaner or more disagreeable than he. He was mourned by a few of his own household when he was buried. After his death no one objected when the widow became the young man's mistress with all her heart. We see them going to church together; they sit down at the table together and go to bed together. Already he calls the lady his mother, and she calls him her son. The man-servants and maid-servants have now become accustomed to calling him their father, and he in turn calls them his children. Never have we seen greater love or a married couple so well suited to each other. Their door, which formerly was closed to widows and orphans, is now always open to rich and poor. There, if you desire, you will have suitable lodgings. Their large house stands at the entrance of our village."

Then the redhead, who was vain and very haughty, asked: "Is there any old man here, who has a very beautiful wife?" The shepherd replied: "There is an old man who had a very good wife, but unfortunately she died. He was married again recently to a stupid and exceedingly bold young lady. Because she despises him, she regards it as nothing to deceive him frequently and dishonorably with her stupid suitors."

FRAGMENT VII

(The redhead was pleased to hear that there was a promiscuous young lady with an old husband and decided to spend the night at their house. Ruodlieb, on the other hand, remembered the great king's advice and stayed at the home of the young man who was married to the old wife. This couple charitably fed all the poor people of the village.)

He cut the bread and distributed it among them, and some meat fell to their share from six tables. After they had been consoled and had happily returned to their homes, the host also said: "Whenever Christ sends anyone to me, my household and I must celebrate Easter just as on this night when we are gladdened by you. It seems to me that God is sending to me what comes from you." Then the host offered Ruodlieb a piece of shoulder and a piece of leg, which he cut into many minute pieces and divided among all the servants as sacraments. After this much cooked food and much roasted meat were placed before the lord. A drink of excellent wine and of peppery mead was brought in a walnut cup of the best veined wood, on which were carved four rivers in gold. The right hand of God was represented on the very bottom of the cup, which a certain noble had given to the host when he had spent the night there. Nevertheless, the host never tasted from it unless the guest whom he served with it offered it to him. The cup was saved for this purpose alone. After the meal was over and water had been given to them, wine was brought to the host, from which he drank; then he offered it to his guest, who first gave it to the lady and afterward drank of it himself. The knight rose from the table and reclined a little while. As he lay, he thought how he might thank his host. At last he readily gave his cloak to the lady of the house so that, thus adorned, she might be able to go to the holy church.

Meanwhile, let us not pass over what the redhead was doing. When the knight entered the house where he found so many good things, the redhead asked him why he went where an old she-ape was. The knight replied: "Choose to come along with me. Later perhaps you may be glad that you did. I have found what I wanted, and you will soon have what you are looking for." Many who were standing near the redhead advised him not to leave his companion, since he would not find better lodgings anywhere. Without delay, however, the redhead departed from the knight disdainfully and hurried to his "cousin"—nothing but death was in store for him. He found the gate of the old man's house barred with a fence around it. The old man and his two sons in front of him were standing in the yard. The redhead knocked and said, shaking the gate hard: "Open up as quickly as possible and don't leave me outside!" When the old man said, "Look through the fence to see who it is," his boy ran back and replied, "The man is shaking and breaking down the gate!" The redhead said: "Open up! You inquire as if you didn't know me!" At this the angry youths began to quarrel with him. Fearing the force of evil, the old man ordered that the gate be opened for the redhead. He rushed into the yard very boldly and haughtily and did not take off his cap but, jumping from his horse and tossing the reins of his bridle around a stake, he drew his sword as if he were insane and stood before them like a heathen. Finally, laughing, he said to the old man: "I am surprised that you are keeping silent about whether you know me." The old man replied: "I do not know who you are. You are acting very foolishly. Now I do not know who you are or what you want of us." "Your wife is a very close cousin of mine. Allow me to speak to her alone." The old man replied, "Do so!" and ordered his wife to come to him. She came. As soon as the redhead saw her, he desired her, burning in his heart. Rejoicing, he smiled at her, and she, rejoicing with him, smiled back. "Your father and mother send you their best wishes. Later, wherever you wish, I shall tell you everything else when we are alone." Then they stood at the gate and leaned on the fence. The redhead said: "First, mark attentively what I say, for our conversation must not be long. Don't weep, don't laugh, but contain yourself seriously so that the old dog won't become wise to our intentions. If you consent to me, you will be freed from him quickly. For there is a young man, full of every kind of virtue, who is neither short nor tall but of average height. He is completely white like fine wheat flour but ruddy in his cheeks, and in the whole world there is no one more handsome than he. When he learned how beautiful you are and what daily hardships you endure, he grieved from the bottom of his heart and said to me with a sigh: 'If ever you were faithful to me, dear friend, go and tell that tortured woman that if she wishes me to free her and remove her from her prison, she should speak to no woman, even one loyal to her, and should leave the yard tomorrow when she hears the soft horn resounding and stand on the street in concealment until I run up with many persons to seize her. Then she may be my mistress and do whatever she pleases.' Now, my dear cousin, send him whatever message you wish." She stood with self control when she heard all this and although rejoicing within, nevertheless said to him as if she were sad: "Be assured that I will do everything gladly, for I give you my word." After her right hand was taken, the redhead, doubting no further, said: "For pay, I want you to promise to lie with me three times." "Do it ten times if you can or as often as you wish," she replied. He said: "I'll act as if I wish to leave, but you prevent it." He returned to the old man and said, "Bid me leave!" The old man would have done it gladly if he had been able to in spite of his wife, who asked him repeatedly not to allow the redhead to leave. Her husband consented: "If he wishes, he may remain here. What we have is his." She led the redhead's horse into the stable hastily, but neither she nor the redhead paid any more attention to the animal, which was left on its own to eat hay if it could find any there.

The redhead's "cousin" received him cordially when he entered the house. They sat down together and played a lot during the course of their conversation. They clasped hands and kissed each other. The old man entered, and no one was more serious than he. His face was so hairy that no one could see what it looked like (because it was very shaggy) except for his nose alone, which was bent and crooked. His two eyes were dark as if they had been scratched out, and a forest of twisted hair overshadowed them. No one could see where the opening to his mouth was, so long and thick was the beard which covered it. He ordered the servants to prepare much to eat. Since the excessive play of those two was displeasing to him, he sat down between them and separated them with his buttocks. For a little while they were silent and grieved because they had been separated. Bending forward in front of him, they talked and joked about many things. When the old man became disgusted, he ordered that the table be covered and said to his wife: "That's enough! Now cease from your shameful behavior! A woman ought not to be so bold, nor should a man be either! When one's husband is present, one should not play with a stranger!" Having thus spoken, he got up as if to go to the toilet but looked back at them through a peephole. The redhead—unfortunately for him—leaped into the old man's seat. One hand touched her breasts and the other, her legs, but she concealed them with her fur coat by spreading it over them. The old man observed all this, spying like a thief. When he returned, the redhead did not yield his seat to him, for she would not allow him to. Then, sitting down at the head of the table very indignantly, the old man frequently advised his wife to order that dinner be served. She, however, delayed the meal by mocking her husband and joking. He asked the servants whether dinner was ready. "You can dine as soon as you like," they replied. "Now, my wife, let us dine and go to bed. It is also time for your dear friend to rest. You have thoroughly exhausted him. Now allow him to rest!"

FRAGMENT VIII

(During the night that the redhead spent at the home of the old man who was married to the promiscuous young wife, he had intercourse with her as previously agreed and was caught in the act by her husband, who was then mortally wounded by the redhead after a terrible fight. A priest was called to perform the final rites of the Church for the dying man.)

The priest came and wished to preach the Holy Creed to him. The dying man had no strength except to say with frequent groans, "I believe." The priest asked him whether he repented of the evil which he had done. With nods and words he showed that he was penitent. He was made pure of all his sin through the body of the Lord. As he lay dying, he entrusted his soul to the Lord, saying: "Merciful Christ, have pity on a very guilty man, forgive them who have taken my life, and inspire my sons, I beseech You, to do the same." Thus speaking, he became silent and soon afterward passed away.

When the day dawned, people assembled from everywhere, and before the church itself was a large gathering of his neighbors, both great and small. The judge came there as soon as he learned of the miserable crime. When those whose right it was to sit down had taken their seats there, the judge said: "This is certainly miserable news that a man who was better than everyone was beaten to death." Weeping, all who were sitting there said: "Unless he is avenged, we know that the same thing will happen again."

The judge sent for the children and at the same time for the murderers themselves. When they came and stood before the judge, the redhead laughed, and the guilty woman looked down at the ground. When the judge saw that the redhead was laughing, he said: "Most evil man, do you laugh when you see all of us here weeping? Why did you become so inflamed that you tortured him like that?" The red-haired man replied: "He knocked out my front teeth for no reason except that I sat beside my cousin." The judge said: "If the young maid was your cousin, why did you defile her and add crime to crime?" The redhead answered: "Why did this bitch allure me to her? Why should I seek to do it? I should not have done it if she had not begged me." She cried so much that she made a stream of tears there. From her eyes then flowed much blood. After she recovered so that she could say something, she said: "O you very faithless man, why do you lie so about me? You follow Adam's example, who put the blame on Eve. I did not send for you. I had not seen you before, you wicked man! You deceived me with false promises. I do not defend what I did, but rather I condemn what you have done and committed with my advice. I do not desire to take vengeance on my own behalf, I admit. Judge, postpone making the decision for a little while until I accuse and also condemn myself. Look, I stand as my own judge. I shall endure this very willingly. If you wish that I be hanged from a big tree, cut off my hair and braid a long rope of it so that I may be strangled by that which often made me guilty. But I ask that you remove my corpse after three days and burn it and throw the ashes into water so that the sun may not hide its radiance or the air refuse the rain or the hail be said to harm the world because of me. If you wish to submerge me enclosed in a vessel, mark on the outside of the vessel what crime I have committed so that those who find me dare not bury me. Only let them break the vessel and throw me back into the water so that I may quickly be devoured by fish or dire crocodiles. If you wish to thrust me into a fiery, smoky furnace, I shall enter of my own accord so that I may not be consumed by the fire of hell. If you wish that I lose my life submerged in a sewer (I am very dirty and very worthy of such a punishment), I shall fall in promptly because I rejoice in such an end, lest I later have to endure the stench of hell. Whatever punishment even more severe that you find, I shall endure it all willingly for I deserve much worse." When she became silent, the judge, moved by compassion, thus spoke: "She is judging herself. Say whether this is enough." All, weeping and sympathizing with her completely, said: "It is not necessary for the judge to ask any more about this." The jurors said: "We decide that life be given to her only insofar as she repents of her evil deed." Her stepsons, having become as gentle as lambs, cast themselves at the feet of the judge and entreated that he grant her life, pardon, and well-being and that he allow her to be the lady of the house as she had been before. When he promised this mercifully, she refused it: "Let them call me from now on not a lady but a murderess. But, if you wish me to live, I beg, nevertheless, that you take away from me just enough of my soundness of body so that you will not completely debilitate me. Cut off my nose and my lips so that my teeth will be horrible without any covering and no one henceforth will want to kiss me. Burn deeply the form of a cross on both my cheeks, which until now have shone with a reddish glow like roses, so that everyone may know that this was done on account of my crime and may say, 'Woe to you! Do you deserve such a punishment for yourself?', lest my great guilt remain entirely unpunished." Then the judge entrusted her to the children of the old man so that she might be a mother and a mistress to them, not a stepmother as before.

She cast aside all her beautiful clothes and ornaments and put on a coat, which looked as if it were dyed in soot. She shaved her hair and plaited from it little cords with which she tied her tender breasts together. The cords cut into her flesh with force until it decayed. A ragged covering covered her whole head. Thus nothing but her nose and eyes could be seen. She learned the Psalter and sang it for the soul of the old man. She did not eat except when she saw the evening star (then she ate only dry bread, which was dark and ashy) and drank only three spoonfuls of water. She walked bare-footed through cold and heat and slept on a bed covered with nothing but chaff and having only a wooden block for a pillow. She got up before dawn and prayed on her knees at the tomb of the old man where she remained until she began to perspire and could no longer stand up. Then she fell on her face after making a fountain of tears there. Whether it was snowing or raining or whether the sun burned hotly, she went to church as soon as the bells were rung and did not return to her home until it became day everywhere. Then she returned for a short while and remained there until she had washed her face and the priest had rung the bell for celebrating the Mass. Then she returned to church and stayed there until the ninth hour. She claimed no authority for herself but left it all to her stepsons. She took whatever they gave her and did not seek what they did not give. She never laughed after this nor ever joked with anyone. When others laughed, she had only sweet tears. Henceforth no one saw her angry or quarreling or dissolute so long as she lived.

After she had been entrusted to the sons and received by them, the judge said to the people: "Tell me, what are we to do with the redhead, who committed this double and mournful crime among us?" The redhead, certain of a verdict of death, said: "I have a comrade here. Have him called, I beseech you, before you ask what the punishment should be for these crimes. He can thoroughly tell you of what sort I am." When the people, desirous of the knight's presence, wanted to send for him, the knight's host said: "The man whom you wish will soon be here. He stayed at my house last night because he was not like that scoundrel over there." When the host produced him, the judge asked the knight standing before him: "Tell us, noble knight, is this man your friend?"

FRAGMENT IX

(The rest of the episode about the redhead has unfortunately not survived, but it is almost certain that he was convicted by the court and sentenced to death.

On his way home Ruodlieb met a cousin, who was having an affair with a prostitute. Ruodlieb wanted him to accompany him home, but the cousin first desired to confess to Ruodlieb about his relationship with the whore. Ruodlieb restrained him with these words:)

"When the time comes, you will be permitted to say everything. Now order a horse to be saddled for yourself and for one vassal. For our fellow countrymen know you better than they do me. When they see you, they will shun me completely. You ought to go home if you have any regard for me." Immediately this gladdened his heart, and he wept with joy. "Stop!" the knight said.

FRAGMENT X

RUODLIEB AND HIS COUSIN VISIT A CHATELAINE

(Ruodlieb succeeded in persuading his cousin to return home with him and, accompanied by two squires, they set out on the trip. They first came to a castle, where a widowed chatelaine, who was a friend of Ruodlieb's mother, lived with her daughter.)

There was a closet there nearly in concealment, in which many nails were fixed in the wall on which travellers could hang all their things so that mice would not harm them. They were not afraid of thieves there. The chatelaine went with the lords to the high balcony where she said to them: "Now be very welcome!" When they thanked her, she asked them to sit down and to joke with her.

(Ruodlieb demonstrated to the chatelaine his ability to catch fish with bugloss.)

The knight said: "Now we shall fish with the powder of bugloss, with which we fished before." There was a boat in the water. They took a stick. The fish came and ate the pellets. After they tasted them, they could not leap back into the water. The knight, frightening the fish with the stick, drove them to land. The chatelaine and her retinue of young ladies were amazed, and Ruodlieb's relative rejoiced in his skills. There was loud laughter and applause.

The cooks ran up, took the fish, and then hurried to prepare them. When he stepped out of the boat, Ruodlieb, accompanied by all the people, returned to the chatelaine, who received him cordially: "There is nowhere such a fisherman as you are." Then she bade them place the fish out on the soft grass so that she might see how many different kinds that lake produced. Then all that had been caught there were spread out: the pike and the gurnard, which are the wolves among fish since they devour fish whenever they can catch them; the bream, the salmon, the carp, the tench, the barbel, and the orf; the chub and the nosefish, both of which are very bony inside; the bottom-dwelling burbot; two species of trout, both red and white; the headfish which has a large head and is deficient in fins in back; the slippery eel and the catfish, horrible because of its head; the grayling and the Rhine lake-trout, both quite pleasant to eat; the perch, which has a sharp back and pierces like a needle. Moreover, there were many fish which are not well known to me. After she saw them, the chatelaine ordered that they be taken away and quickly prepared. The table was set and was heaped with rolls which had been brought. Meanwhile she sent for her daughter to come quickly, and immediately many agile young servants ran after her. She was weaving two bands of gold for whatever fiancé the clemency of Christ would someday give her. When she came forth, she shone like the clear moon. No one could discern how adroit she was. No one could tell whether she flew or swam or how she moved.

(Ruodlieb and his cousin were guests of the chatelaine at dinner.)

Then the chatelaine asked for water, which she bade the young lady to take. Afterward it was given to her guests, and she herself received it last after them. The older man sat by the older woman, and the younger man sat beside the young lady. The young lady became the table companion of Ruodlieb's relative. Only one cup and only one plate were given to them. In their presence was a dog, which could disclose every theft. Turning its face around, it coaxed with its tail and reminded them to give it something. The dog took whatever Ruodlieb's relative gave it of his own accord but did not go after what fell to it by chance. But if he gave the dog something and said, "Taste this! An evil man cooked it," the dog would never taste it or would vomit up what it had tasted. A waiter stole Ruodlieb's spurs. Later when the waiter asked that he hand him the dishes immediately, as is the custom with all waiters, the dog kept looking at him fiercely, finally jumped upon him, pulled at his clothing, tore it to pieces, and would have bitten him if the squire had not pulled the dog away. The knight laughed, and all the rest of the people were amazed. Then the chatelaine said: "This thing seems strange to me." The knight said to the thief: "The dog is aware of that theft of yours. Unless you give back what you stole, you will die. Go and bring quickly into the open the article which you stole!" Running, the thief brought back the two spurs without delay. "These," he said, "I stripped from your saddle a little while ago. There was no one there then, and no living person saw me. The dog would not know if it had not learned about it from the devil." The knight said: "Give them to the dog and see to whom it offers them!" When he threw them to the dog, it returned them to whom they belonged. Ruodlieb said to the dog: "Now take them back to my companion." It gave them to the squire, wagging its tail again and again. "Fall before the feet of the thief and ask for pardon!" The dog prostrated itself, placed its head at the thief's feet, and as if it were weeping, howled, asking for pardon. "Now say, 'Rise and let us be friends as before!'" When the thief had said this, the dog got up and rejoiced, thanked first the thief, then its masters, and then those who were seated. The knight said: "One of you grab the thief by the hair and take a stick as if to punish his crime." When two did this and asked, "Why did you steal?", the dog leaped on them and freed him from them, biting on their calves the two attackers, who were going to be very sorry that they had so mocked the man with whom the dog had previously been reconciled. Some laughed and others were quite astonished at this. The food at the dinner was very sumptuous. After many courses and as many drinks, water was brought. They sat a short time while they drank. It was not then the season for any kind of fruits, but boys came and brought strawberries from the forest—some in vessels, some in hazel bark—which they had picked one by one everywhere. After these were eaten, the table was removed and water was provided.

(Ruodlieb and his cousin retired to change their clothes.)

They went to take off their shoes. Ruodlieb encircled his legs with bands bought in Lucca. And over his silk puttees he wore shoes. Ruodlieb's relative wore red socks under decorated cordovan shoes. He bound both his legs with two bands. From them hung down many ornaments all around. Then he put on a parti-colored skin coat slashed in front and back and adorned all around with marten throat-fur. He also put on a long fur cloak with a very wide and black beaver border. He took the ring which the young lady had given him and which barely fitted on his little finger. Soon they returned to the ladies whom they found at the gallery balustrade, looking out.

FRAGMENT XI

(The chatelaine's birds were one source of amusement to the guests.)

The birds ate very much themselves and then gave food to their young. When someone offered them crumbs through the openings in their cage, they quickly hurried there with their mouths open, seizing eagerly whatever could reach them. After a short while all the birds soon became accustomed to do this. But later, when the door of their cage was opened, they perched on the hands of various persons and took what was given them. When they became satiated and were smooth from having been stroked by the hand, they soon returned voluntarily and eagerly to their cage, arranged their feathers with their beaks, and perched. They were so happy that they were not silent for the whole day. This became a pleasant delight for the young lady, although all such things were very disagreeable to the older people. No food or water was in the cage of the starlings, and the people caused them to be overcome by hunger so that they would demand that food be given them through the openings. The old parents persistently refused this at first. Since they did not give anything to their young, their young left them and soon opened their mouths wide for those who stuck in their fingers. A qualified teacher was chosen to teach them to speak in our language and to recite the Lord's Prayer as far as "Who art in Heaven," "-ven" being repeated three times. Sister Staza was also to teach them to repeat "sing" twice. The young starlings learned this before the old ones were able to.

Meanwhile the knight and his relative went together with the chatelaine to where the harpists were playing. When the knight heard how badly the best student of this art among them played the melody, he asked the chatelaine whether there was another harp there. "Here is a harp," she said, "and there will never be one any better. My husband played it as long as he was alive. Because of its sound my heart becomes weak with love. No one has touched it since he died. If you wish, you can play melodies on it." She ordered that it be brought to him, and he hastened to play it. Striking the chords sometimes with two fingers of his left hand and touching them at other times with his right, he produced very sweet melodies. He made all variations very distinctly so that one who was completely ignorant of dancing and of keeping time with his hands quickly learned both these things. Those who formerly had struck the chords boldly and jestingly listened silently and dared not play. When the knight had finished playing three unusual melodies very pleasantly, the chatelaine and her daughter asked him to play a fourth, to which his relative and the young lady could dance. While he was playing it admirably and excellently and was giving responses in scales and intervals, the young man got up and the young lady rose opposite him. He turned round like a falcon and she, like a swallow. As soon as they came together, they quickly glided past each other. He seemed to be moving and she, to be swimming, so that no one could have improved either their dancing or their keeping of time with their hands, even if he had wanted to. Then by lowering their hands they gave a sign—which many there regretted—that the dance was over. They sat down together and burned with great love for each other, desiring to be joined in marriage. Her mother wished exceedingly that this happen and made it possible for them to talk about what they wanted to. The young lady asked her lover to play dice with her on the condition that the ring of the loser be given to the one who would win three times. Then he said: "No, let both rings belong to the one of us who wins the first game which we shall now play." She approved of this and defeated him in play. The young man lost gladly and gladly gave her his ring. Very happy that she had thus received the prize of victory, she quickly lost in play her own ring, which she pulled from her finger and threw to him with a spin. In the middle of this ring there was a hollow knot inside. Unless he had loosened it, he would not have been able to put the ring on his finger.

FRAGMENT XII

(Ruodlieb and the chatelaine discussed his cousin and his mother, whom she knew well.)

"Now, my lady, tell me how recently you have seen my mother. Tell me if she is well and if her situation is peaceful. Since she became your godmother, tell me whether I have a brother whom you raised from the baptismal font, or whether she raised your daughter from the font." The chatelaine was quite stunned by these words of the knight: "Oh, what have you said? Do you think that she whose very life is not pleasant without you has married? She has already lost her sight because of weeping for you. She raised my daughter from the baptismal font and from that time on has considered both of us as her own daughters. She visits us often and then brings us something." When the knight heard this, he felt sympathy for his mother and asked, weeping: "Can I return home this week?" The chatelaine replied: "You can see your dear mother tomorrow night, but I wish to be the first to obtain the messenger's bread at her house." It was made public that the knight was the son of the godmother. There quickly arose great joy among the servants, who rejoiced with the mother on account of the safe return of her son. Then the chatelaine sent a messenger, whom she ordered to tell the godmother that the latter's son would return that very day.

In the meantime, the young man and the young lady played dice together. She beat him three times, and he defeated her just as often. Defeated by each other, they rejoiced in the good omen of the agreement because he belonged to the girl and she belonged to him. They were glad that they had not won but had been defeated. She was called his in the masculine form, and vice versa he was called hers in the feminine form. In speaking to each other, they mixed up their genders and made a type of grammatical error. No longer did they conceal that they loved each other passionately. If the mother had allowed, they would have slept together that very night. Nevertheless, she would have permitted it if it had not been dishonorable to them. Then the girl could hardly be prevailed upon to wait.

(After arrangements for the marriage of Ruodlieb's cousin and the chatelaine's daughter were made, Ruodlieb and his relative set out for home.)

RUODLIEB RETURNS HOME

(Three messengers, sent by Ruodlieb's mother, met him on the way, and a servant awaited his arrival from the top of a cherry tree.)

A servant sat in a tree, watching from there and scorning the cherries hanging before him. He wanted to be the first to announce his master's arrival. Above him there was a jackdaw investigating what he was doing and why he was abstaining from the cherries. It observed whatever he did and said so that it might later disclose this to Ruodlieb's mother. The servant desired more to see his master riding toward him than to eat the cherries. He constantly said to himself: "Ruodlieb, my master, hurry and come!" The jackdaw learned this, flew back to the lady, and spoke to her as follows: "Please listen to what I now have to say!" She said, "Speak!" The jackdaw replied, "Ruodlieb, my master, hurry and come!" Although the servants saw their mistress sighing, all of them laughed at the fact that the bird had observed such a thing. Ruodlieb's mother said: "Fly back, perch above the servant and note what he says! If he shouts, you shout too!" The jackdaw listened to the words of that servant who was eager for Ruodlieb's arrival. At last the servant beheld his friends emerging from the dense forest. First came the relative, beside whom was his squire. Finally the lord and his squire appeared. Then the servant shouted: "Rejoice, my master is approaching!"

FRAGMENT XIII

(The jackdaw reported these words to Ruodlieb's mother. After they arrived home, Ruodlieb and his cousin prepared themselves for the banquet which Ruodlieb's mother had arranged in his honor.)

He shaved so that not even one hair was left there. No one was so clever that he could discern whether he was a cleric or a woman or a beardless pupil because he had a face so pleasant and so maidenly. After they had shaved and had washed away their dirt with water, they got out of the tub. The squire at once put bathrobes around them, and, covered with these, they went to the couch and remained there until they had become dry and had cooled off. After a little while they got up and asked for their shoes.

Then the knight stepped to the table. Yet he did not wish to sit at the head of the table but sat humbly on the right of his mother like a guest and gladly permitted her to have all the authority. He respectfully took what she gave him. Cutting the bread, she divided it among all the group and passed to everyone a dish of special foods, serving a bowl of wine and sometimes one of mead. Ruodlieb's relative was his eating companion. Both ate from one loaf and from one plate and drank together from one cup. The jackdaw was accustomed to be the mother's only dining companion. When she gave it a crumb, it took it and, strutting along proudly, leaped diagonally across the whole table.

After many courses and as many following drinks, the lady asked for water, and the chamberlain brought it. She ordered that it be given to all the nobles at every table. Afterward the cupbearers served a drink to everybody. When the tables had been removed and the tablecloths had been folded up, they rose happily and thanked the lady. They said that they were glad that Ruodlieb had returned safe and sound to console his mother lest she be distressed any longer as she had been often before when she had grieved that she was without him. It was quickly made known throughout the whole region that Ruodlieb had returned very copiously enriched.

When he later chose and was given privacy, he entered his room with his beloved mother and ordered his squire to bring his pack. From this he took numerous precious riches and some other treasure consisting of fur cloaks and skin coats, which he had obtained in his ten years as an exile. Then he asked for his knapsacks, both of which the squire brought. Ruodlieb ordered him to take out the loaves made in the land of the Africans. When the squire produced them, Ruodlieb said to his mother jestingly: "Mother, I earned these at the place where I have been until this time. The king gave them to me and forbade me to break them until now." His mother said: "I think we should first call the servants so that they may see how good

African loaves taste." Ruodlieb said: "I think it would be better if we alone see them."

Pulling out a knife, with which he cut one loaf, he perceived the silver of the dish, under which there was gold. When he scratched away the flour, the radiance of the silver was resplendent. Seeing that the dishes were joined together with nails in three places, he quickly rubbed down the little heads of the nails with a file, loosened the dishes, and saw there golden coins joined so closely that no more could have been forced in. Ruodlieb rejoiced exceedingly and gave thanks to the Lord. Not delaying to pick up the similar dish in his hands, he wiped away the flour and filed down the nails minutely. He saw that the dish was filled with coins and with various treasure, and was astonished. His mother exulted exceedingly. Then, uttering sighs with moistened eyes but rejoicing very much in her heart, she gave thanks to Christ in heaven that He had given her a son so enriched and so blessed. The knight cast himself to the ground and again and again pressed the earth with his lips as if he were throwing himself before the feet of the King, his Lord. Then weeping a lot and wetting his face with tears, he prayed: "O Lord, who can be equal to You, who mercifully deign thus to enrich and to increase with honors a poor little man such as I, but not to remember that You have suffered on account of my sins? Now, O Lord, I pray, grant to me that I will not die before I see again the king to whom I came poor and needy and who received me kindly at Your request and made me a participant in such great delights.

Keeping me, a poor man, with him for ten years, he enriched me so that now I can live very honorably and confidently if I manage these things wisely." After Ruodlieb and his mother had rejoiced greatly over this situation, they closed the dishes as carefully as they could and took along all the other treasure he had brought with him. Many of their younger servants then ran toward them.

FRAGMENT XIV

(Ruodlieb made all the arrangements for the wedding of his cousin. He asked his mother to invite the chatelaine's daughter to their house and was speaking to his mother when this fragment begins:)

"Invite some of our dear relatives to come so that they may be present when this marriage is contracted. Invite that girl to your home now and ask your mutual friends to come." After the girl had arrived and her relatives stood around her, the court quickly became full of friends, who had come for the occasion. Ruodlieb received them cordially and kissed them. He asked them to have lunch and gave them much to eat. After the tables were removed, the ladies returned to their chambers, and the daughter preceded them. After them walked servants who carried feather pillows for them, and many others accompanied them to be of service. Ruodlieb ordered that wine be brought to them in return for their service. After each one drank, he gave the bowl to his neighbor, and finally the cupbearers returned the emptied bowl. They bowed, departed, and returned to Ruodlieb and the lords.

Then Ruodlieb said: "Because God has assembled you here, now listen to me and take care to support me so that a certain marriage, which has been agreed upon and committed to us, may now be contracted. I desire that you be present with me as witnesses of this marriage. It happens that my young cousin and the young lady fell in love with each other when they were playing dice and desire to be united in marriage." They said: "All of us should advise that a man of such great natural ability and of such excellent virtue be not dishonored but quickly snatched away from a vile whore, who very much deserves to be burned by fire." They praised the Lord that somewhere in this world there was a woman who would tear that witch away from him. Then the young man got up and thanked them because they were all so kind to him. He said that he shuddered deeply and was very much ashamed that he had been so dishonored by that accursed whore. "Now you see that I have much need of a wife. Since we can now find her here easily, I desire that she be betrothed to me and joined to me in marriage. I ask that you be willing witnesses when we shall present wedding gifts to each other, as is the custom." They replied: "We shall support you readily in this matter." Ruodlieb sent for the three ladies together, and they came quickly with the daughter preceding them. The line of guests rose to honor them. When all had sat down and had been silent for a short while, Ruodlieb got up and asked them to listen to him. He then told his relatives and friends of the couple's agreement and said that they were burning with love for each other. They asked the young man whether he desired to have the young lady as his wife. They asked her whether she desired him. She smiled a little and then replied: "I should not refuse a servant defeated in a game, whom I beat with dice under the obligation of an agreement that whether he won or lost, he would marry only me. I wish that he serve me vigorously night and day. The better he does this, the dearer he will be to me." Then all laughed loudly because she had spoken so boldly and in such a friendly manner. When they perceived that her mother did not disapprove of the marriage and that the families of both were equal in influence and in wealth, they carefully decided that the couple were well suited for each other and were of the opinion that she should be promised to him in marriage. Then the bridegroom drew his sword and wiped it at its point. Set in the hilt was a golden ring, which the bridegroom offered to his bride with these words: "Just as the ring embraces your whole finger, so I pledge to you my firm and perpetual fidelity. You should perserve this for me or be beheaded." She responded to the young man very intelligently and fitly: "Both of us should be subject to the same decision. Tell me, why should I keep better fidelity to you than you keep to me? Tell me whether you can maintain that Adam would have been permitted to have a mistress in addition to Eve, when God made his rib into only one woman. When Adam cried out that his rib had been taken from him, tell me where you have read that two Eves were granted him. When you were fornicating with whores, would you have wanted me to be your whore? It shall not happen that I be joined to you on these terms. Go! Goodbye! Whore however much you like but without me! There are so many men in the world like you whom I can marry so easily!" Having thus spoken, she left him his sword and ring. The young man said to her: "My sweetheart, it will be as you wish. If ever I do this, may I lose the property which I have given you, and may you have power of cutting off my head." She smiled a little and, turning back to him, said: "Let us now be united on this condition without deceit." Her suitor said "Amen" and kissed her.

After they were so joined, the praise of the people was very great. Praising the Lord, they sang the wedding song. Ruodlieb gave the bridegroom a skin coat very well adorned with marten throat-fur and a fur cloak brushing along the ground with its border. He also gave him a swift horse very magnificently adorned with trappings. He presented gifts to the bride, who had been joined in wedlock to his relative. To her he gave three brooches to cover her beautiful breast and four decorated bracelets. He also gave her three rings adorned with jewels and an ermine cloak covered with scarlet cloth. The rest of the group gave their large wedding gifts to them. What do I care how they later got along with each other?

FRAGMENT XV

RUODLIEB'S COURTSHIP

(After the marriage of Ruodlieb's cousin, Ruodlieb's mother began to urge her son to think about getting married himself. She spoke to him about old age as follows:)

"Old age, which spares no one, overcomes all alike. A woman who is like the moon in the flower of her youth becomes like an old she-ape when she reaches old age. In old age her forehead, which once was smooth, is furrowed with wrinkles. Her eyes, which formerly were dove-like, are now dark. Her nose is filled with mucus and drips filth. Her cheeks, once taut with fat, now sag. Her snaggleteeth, through which her tongue pushes out words when she speaks, are loose as if they were ready to fall out. She utters a word as though her mouth were full of flour. Now her chin is curved and turned up, and her once smiling mouth, which attracted many, is always open and apt to frighten people. Her neck is now thin like that of a featherless magpie. Her breasts, which once stuck out like inflated balls, now hang flabby like mushrooms without juice. Her hair, formerly golden-colored, which hung down to her buttocks in separate pieces and covered her back in braids, sticks up horribly, frightening onlookers, as if her head had been drawn through a hedge, buttocks first. She is stooped over, and her head is overshadowed by her projecting shoulders like a slow vulture when he knows that a carcass lies dead. She who had been accustomed to go ungirt in her youth now tucks her coat up high to keep from getting it dirty when she stamps on beans in order to make porridge from them. Her shoes, which formerly were quite close-fitting, are now loose even with stockings and, turned up at the toe like a hoe, pick up much slimy mud when she walks. Her thin fingers, once full of fat and not dried up but now merely bones over fleshless skin, are very dirty from soot with their shrivelled knuckles and with their long uncut nails, black with filth. In the same way that it overcomes a woman does old age overcome an agile youth.

(Ruodlieb's mother then described the effects of old age on a man.)

"'Death, you who alone are the end of human misfortunes, why do you come to me late? Why do you not release me from my prison?' Although this life is death for him, he must wait until his soul passes away when God commands. For this law prevails over everything that exists, whether it fly, walk, or swim: That which has a beginning will not lack an end." Ruodlieb's mother, who was so weak that she could not escape death, did not cease, however, to admonish her son frequently.

FRAGMENT XVI

(Ruodlieb's mother continued to urge her son to get married and produce an heir:)

"If you have no son, you will have no heir! Tell me, my son, what will happen if you die without children? There will be a violent dispute concerning our property. The strength of my youth completely fails me, for during the ten years when you were among the Africans, I was daily distressed with cares at every hour, grieving for you and for having to protect our property. If you had not returned, I should soon have become blind. But I began to feel young when I learned that you were returning home. Now I am holding myself together better than my strength allows. I should desire, if you do, that we now summon our relatives and loyal friends so that with their advice and loyal help you can find a wife, who you know is of such parentage on both sides that your offspring in turn may not be defective on either side and by whose character your honor may not be lessened. May merciful God point her out to you and join her to you in marriage." Ruodlieb answered his mother very gently: "Tomorrow let us send a message to our relatives and friends to assemble at our castle as quickly as possible. If you think that the advice which they will give me should be acted upon, I shall not neglect it but shall carry out whatever you wish."

Messengers were sent and the friends were assembled. After they had arrived at the castle and had been received cordially, Ruodlieb arranged the seats as he well knew how and specified in which place each one should sit, giving one table to every two lords. And he ordered that one seat be made higher for his mother so that she could overlook all who were sitting there and could eat alone and thus be able to be seen as the mistress of the castle. So honoring his mother and treating her as mistress, he deserved praise from the people but from the Almighty a crown and a long-lasting, blessed life. After they had finished eating, Ruodlieb asked that the tables be removed. The doors were closed and were watched by two strong men, who did not allow anyone to go in or out until the meeting was concluded. Then Ruodlieb got up and asked that all be silent for a little while in order that he might inform them why he had assembled them. When they became silent, he spoke as his mother had advised him: "Now listen, my relatives and friends! The great sorrow and hardship with which my mother has endured many things and has cared for everything since she was bereft of my father and me is indeed evident to you. Now her strength is failing her, her limbs are growing weak, and from this time forward she will not be able to do what she could formerly, as she frequently tells me and as I see myself. Hence she does not cease from advising me to get married. Therefore, I just now sent for you to come so that each of you might reflect upon this and give me his advice, for very few women are known to me, and I do not know where to turn to my advantage. Tell me what you can do about this situation, whether you can find me a wife who will not disgrace our family but will gild it with her character and her inherited nobility of life!" They responded together: "We shall do this as joyfully as possible so that we may see born to you a dear son who will be the heir of the character, virtues, and blessings with which Christ has enriched and honored you." Each one nodded approval and promised to do this. But one man, to whom the regions and the lords, who were the highest there, were well known, rose and said: "I know one young lady, who is equal to you in integrity of character, in virtue, and in nobility. I should like you to see her so that when you have, you may admit that you have never seen any young lady in the world who practices every virtue so zealously as she does. She is so remarkable that she would make any man proud."

FRAGMENT XVII

(Ruodlieb agreed to consider the young lady, but after an investigation, discovered that she was having an affair with a priest. He even obtained her hat and knee bands which she had left with the priest. Ruodlieb sent a messenger to the young lady with a proposal of marriage and a box containing the two items without telling him what the contents were. The messenger was well received and first extended to her Ruodlieb's marriage proposal before producing the box just as he was getting ready to leave.)

Bringing now the best wine in a bowl and at other times sweet mead in golden vessels, she stood and inquired about the girls of his homeland—what reputation they had and whether they were beautiful and honorable. He replied with a smile: "I do not know at all the answer to your questions. I have concerned myself with nothing less than paying attention to what our ladies are doing. Such behavior I leave to the man about town. If I pass by anywhere where I see ladies standing, I bow to them and go where my inclination is to go. What do you wish, my lady, to reply to Ruodlieb through me?" She said: "Give him now from my faithful heart just as much love as there is foliage, give him as much affection as birds have joy, and give him as much honor as there are grass and flowers." After the messenger, who did not doubt at all that she would marry Ruodlieb, had asked to be dismissed, he suddenly became unable to speak and, as if he were stunned, could scarcely speak on account of his groans: "What has happened to me—how bad and how wrong it is—I am ashamed to say. Nothing worse has ever befallen anyone. For Ruodlieb sent some small gifts to you sealed." From his boot he drew the box in which those gifts were. When she received it, she went away from him in a hurry and, standing at a window, opened the box, in which she saw that there was a fine piece of cloth well secured with four seals of his ring. Wondering much what this was, she broke the seals and loosened the knots of the cloth and found a magnificent purple covering tied up. Opening it, she found her hat and bands for the legs which she had lost on the occasion when she had slept with the priest. When she saw these things and remembered where she had lost them, she trembled violently and became pale and cold throughout her whole body. She doubted that he who was pretending to have forgotten the gifts and was acting very foolishly was aware of what was in the box. "All people have hitherto considered me chaste," she reflected. Here courage began to return strengthened. She returned to the messenger and asked him whether he knew what the gifts, which were thus sealed, were and whether he had been present when Ruodlieb had placed them in the box. By Him, from whom nothing is concealed, he swore that he did not know what the gifts were, wondering why she had asked that because what had been entrusted to him was sealed. Then she said: "Tell your relative and friend that even if there were no other man in the world except him alone and even if he were going to give me the whole world as a wedding present, I would be unwilling to marry him—tell him truthfully!" The messenger, who was saddened by this situation, said to the lady: "I wonder why I have come into suspicion." She said: "Immediately be silent! Just go without saying goodbye!"

The messenger departed and hurried back to Ruodlieb. As soon as Ruodlieb saw him, he said to him with a smile: "I know that you were well furnished with drink, well treated, and well filled. Tell me how my message was received. Were my gifts—don't hesitate—well received?" Having thus spoken, he rejoiced and shook with loud laughter. The messenger said that Ruodlieb would lose him as his friend if he made him his messenger again. Ruodlieb said to him seriously: "Tell me now, my relative, what that young lady said when you told her of my great love." The messenger replied: "When I told her in complete detail what your message was, she remained absolutely silent and prepared for me a sumptuous lunch, serving more than enough wine and mead. When I asked her what she wished to reply to you, she said: 'Give him from my faithful heart just as much love as there is foliage, give him as much affection as birds have joy, and give him as much honor as there are grass and flowers.' After I had asked that leave be given me, I suddenly became speechless and told her what my situation was, that I had not given her your gifts—

pretending to have forgotten them. When she received them, she withdrew from me with joy. After a little while she returned and said very indignantly: 'Tell me, if you know, what the gifts are which you have brought.' I swore by Him, the Omnipotent, who knows everything, that I had never seen inside to know what they were. For it was apparent that a knowledge of the sealed contents had been denied me. Then she said: 'Tell your relative and friend that even if there were no other man in the world except him alone and even if he were to give me the whole world as a wedding present, I would be unwilling to marry him—tell him truthfully!' " Ruodlieb spoke: "Now I suppose I must ask for another fiancée, who is not accustomed to love secretly anyone except me."

THE DREAM OF RUODLIEB'S MOTHER

Ruodlieb's mother, insofar as she was able, devoted herself to poor Christians and to widows, orphans, and foreigners. Therefore, she deserved that Ruodlieb be exceedingly blessed. Indeed Christ revealed to her how He wished to glorify him. In her dreams she once saw two wild boars accompanied by a large number of sows, which were threatening with their teeth as if to enter war with Ruodlieb. But her son cut off the head of each wild boar with his sword, and all the striking sows were slaughtered. Afterwards the mother saw a broad and very high linden tree, at whose very top she beheld Ruodlieb sitting on a support.

Around him stood a very large troop on the branches as if ready to wage war. After a little while a beautiful snow-white dove came, carrying in its beak a costly crown adorned with jewels. After placing it on Ruodlieb's head, the dove perched beside him and gave him kisses, which he received and did not refuse. Having seen these things in her dream, the mother meditated upon what all this which she had seen could mean. Although she knew that it symbolized honor, she did not become haughty as a result but remained very humble, attributing not to herself but to the spontaneous mercy of the Lord whatever great honors He would grant to Ruodlieb. After three days she told him what God had revealed to her about the boars whose savage heads he had cut off and about the slaughter of the sows accompanying the two wild boars; how she had seen him sitting on the top of a linden tree and had caught sight of his vassals under him on the branches; and that a dove, flying to him, had brought him a crown, perched in his hands, and given him sweet kisses. "After I saw this, I suddenly woke up and was exceedingly annoyed that I had so awakened. I know that this awakening signifies that I will die before the end of these things comes. My son, remember how often God has helped you in His goodness and has saved you from death itself, and that He often came to your aid in exile and allowed you to return to your fatherland, safe and rich. Now I know that you will obtain greater honors, but I am extremely afraid to say that the Lord rewarded us both whenever we did anything that pleased Him. My son, beware of saying this! For what could we do, who have nothing except what He gives? But whether you fare well or ill, give thanks to Him!"

FRAMENT XVIII

THE EPISODE WITH THE DWARF

(The dream of Ruodlieb's mother was brought to fulfillment. Ruodlieb captured a dwarf who promised him the treasure of two kings, Immunch and his son Hartunch, and Immunch's daughter Heriburg in marriage.)

Leaping up and wishing to get away, the dwarf danced to and fro and shouted until he fell exhausted and barely caught his breath. When his strength returned, he said to Ruodlieb most humbly: "Spare a poor wretch. I'll tell you what I know you want. If you do not kill me and if you free my hands, then I will show you the treasure of two kings, a father and a son, who are going to engage in battle with you. The father's name is Immunch, and his son is Hartunch. You will conquer and destroy both. Then the king's daughter, Heriburg, a very beautiful girl, will be the only surviving heir of the whole kingdom. You will win her but not without great bloodshed unless you do what I advise when I have been set free." Ruodlieb said to the dwarf: "I will not kill you. I would have freed you quickly if I could have trusted you. If you do not deceive me, you will go from me unharmed. When you are free, you will tell me nothing." "May it not happen that this deceit ever prevail among us dwarfs. Then we should be neither of such great age nor of such good health. Among you humans no one speaks except with a deceitful heart. Hence you will not come to mature age. In accordance with the good faith of each one is his period of life. We do not speak otherwise than as we hold in our hearts, nor do we eat various foods which produce sicknesses. For this reason we shall remain sound longer than you. Do not distrust me! I shall act in such a way that you will be able to trust me completely. Nevertheless, if you should distrust me, let my wife be your hostage." He called her from the cave, and she immediately came forth from there. She was small but very beautiful and adorned with gold and clothing. She fell before Ruodlieb's feet and uttered complaints: "Best of all men, free my husband from his chains and hold me in his place until he has accomplished everything!"